THE DUNKELD COLLECTION

HARDY REELS & LURES

WITH PRICE GUIDES

JESS MILLER

First published in 1987 by Jess Miller

Revised, edited, designed, produced and re-published in 2004 by Jess Miller

Text and photographic content © 1987 and 2004 Jess Miller

Website: http://www.HardyReelBook.com

Thanks

Neil Freeman, John Ayers, John Drewett and Roger Still encouraged, cajoled, badgered
and kindly helped me with this book, for which I sincerely thank them.

Dedication

This book is dedicated to the memory of
James Booth, Alan Clout, John McKinley and John Brough

Explanation of Cataloguing Terms

Foot	The part by which the reel is attached to the rod.
Notched Foot	The foot is not smooth having parallel grooves to the underside. Post 1928.
Face Plate	The part of the reel on which the handle is located.
Back Plate	The opposite side of the reel to the face plate.
Tension Screw	Normally a thumb turn disc on the fixed rim of the face plate.
Strapped Tension Screw	Brass strap over tension screw.
Turk's Head Locking Nut	A small extra locking nut found on top of the tension adjuster to prevent the adjuster from moving. Pre 1914.
Check	Mechanism by which adjusted pressure is exerted against fish taking line.
Pawl	Pointed steel piece within check mechanism running against cog on back of faceplate.
Open Ball Race	The ball bearings are not inside a closed race and can easily fall out.
Bridges	The bar supports between the face and back plates.
Waisted	Narrowing in the middle.
Contracted	Narrow Drum.
Lineguard	Nickel Silver, metal or agate lined circular ring or rectangular device through which the line is passed and so prevented from fouling any part of the reel.
Cusps	Small indentations on the rim of the drum.
Drum Core	Central hub of the drum on which the line is mounted.
Caged Drum	A device to increase the size of the drum core consisting of a number of fixed parallel struts between the sides of the drum.
Slotted Drum	Long cut out slots in the drum core.
Multiplier	One turn of the handle produces more than one turn of the drum. A 'multiplying' action.
Leather Case	A Hardy leather reel case.

I have used the following 'star' guide next to each item's number to indicate rarity and to help avoid repetitive description.

*	Fairly Common
**	Not Very Common
***	Rare
****	Extremely Rare
*****	Rarest of All or Unique

Description of overall condition of finish

Worn Finish	Approximately 50% of original finish worn off
Honest Wear	Used, well looked after and worn as one would expect
Lightly Worn	Hardly used
Retaining Most Finish	Approximately 80% of original finish present
Mint	Virtual original condition

Description of overall condition of reels

Fair, Good, Very Good, Excellent, Superb

Logos and Trademarks

Enclosed Oval Logo	
Open Oval Logo	
Straightline Logo	
Hand Trademark	
Shaded Hand Trademark	

Contents

Hardy Reels

Hardy Lures

THE DUNKELD COLLECTION

Introduction to the new Catalogue
Jess Miller

The world of collecting vintage fishing tackle has moved onwards and upwards since the early 1970's.

In 1987 I published the catalogue guide to my Dunkeld Collection of rare Hardy Reels which, along with a number of reference works published since, has served to underpin the collecting of vintage tackle with a sound base of knowledge.

In consequence the genre has not only become established and accepted, but collectable tackle has continued to prove a great investment. Today there are many highly specialised collectors around the world who have developed great knowledge in their particular area of interest and, patronised by these collectors, Angling Auctions of London have established numerous world records for vintage tackle over the last twelve years.

My original catalogue sold out long ago, but so many people have asked me for copies that I am pleased to publish it again, revised and in book format and including a section on Hardy Lures and price guides to every item, which I hope you will find useful.

James Booth became one of antique fishing tackle's trailblazers when he began putting auctions together for Sotheby's from 1980. He was an affable and likeable man who quickly got to grips with his subject and every Sotheby's auction I attended contained the high quality of vintage tackle you would expect from Sotheby's clientele. James very kindly wrote the original Foreword to the 1987 catalogue when he was Director of Sotheby's Sporting Guns & Fishing Tackle Department. Sadly he is no longer with us and I have left his Foreword exactly as he wrote it back then.

This book is dedicated to James and to three of the great characters from the early group of British vintage fishing tackle and angling book collectors who set such great standards for us to follow by conducting themselves in gentlemanly fashion as they went about their collecting.

I am hoping to publish more books on vintage tackle to add to the growing knowledge base that has been driving the collecting of fishing tackle and the preservation of our angling heritage forwards from a hobby enjoyed by a few of us 'eccentrics' back in the late 1960's to a well respected facet of the antiques world of today, in which the rarest fishing related items from our angling history quite rightly command formidable prices.

Photo: Robin Armstrong

THE DUNKELD COLLECTION

Introduction and Profile (1987)
Jess Miller

As a boy of eight in 1957 I came to fish Scotland's famous river Tay. At that age the visit was such an adventure that thereafter I was never able to stay away from this great river for long and eventually, in 1968, my family came to own the 1¾ mile stretch upstream from Telford's historic bridge at Dunkeld in Perthshire.

From boyhood through my teens I was never far from a purring Perfect or screaming Silex. I learned to fly fish for salmon staggering around under the weight of eighteen foot greenheart rods and huge brass reels with a stern teacher who would not let me fish for long if I did not cast properly!

I was lucky enough to be given both new and old handed down Hardy tackle to fish with and one day, whilst rummaging through what had become a morass of rods, reels, baits, flies and boxes with my mentor, desperately seeking out trout flies for a hill loch we were already late to fish, he turned to me and calmly said, "Well, it's a really fine collection of tackle you have now. What a pity that amongst it all we can't find what it is we need to fish with!"

My tackle collecting had surreptitiously begun.

I have been asked many times: What makes a reel rare?

The answer to this question lies in a number of factors which all fishing tackle collectors ought to surely appreciate and yet many, all too often, do not.

The responsibility for their inability to recognise the level of rarity of a particular reel lies in a fairly recent phenomenon, created by the growth of the world tackle collecting market.

After the Second World War and through the 1950's and 1960's you couldn't give old tackle away (or rather that was the accepted method of getting rid of it). It had little or no value and there was a huge 'mountain' of 18th, 19th and 20th century tackle lying dormant in Britain that was collected by only a few people who held a 'hobby' type interest in messing about with old rods, reels and all kinds of piscatorial paraphernalia.

Some fifteen to twenty years ago the market place for fishing tackle existed only through odd auctions, poorly attended by just the few dedicated collectors or those searching for useable items. These auctions were infrequently but consistently held and, very slowly, public interest became aroused. Dealers

appeared and had a field day amongst the large volume of reels that were available to them. Simple adverts brought in droves of tackle that people were only too pleased to see the back of and, naturally, prices began to increase.

The dealers started developing overseas interest and more people began to collect. Over a lengthy period these collectors began to specialise, realising, as did I, that it would be impossible to collect everything that was available. The huge 'mountain' of dormant tackle began to be slowly dissipated and redistributed across the globe. During this period many people became falsely educated into believing that certain rare reels were not in fact really rare at all. They had seen, maybe over ten years, let us say perhaps twenty examples of a certain type of reel, not appreciating at all that these were the nett. examples of that particular model so easily available to the market from the huge untapped stock lying about the country.

Then the biggest surge was created in the market by the American collectors who suddenly began to pour money into Britain, buying up all the finest items. The British collectors fell somewhat by the wayside under this financial onslaught from overseas. Collecting tackle had, unfortunately, become quite a serious business and values were rising too fast and too high for most of them to keep pace with.

We then arrived at the position which will exist for the future whereby the huge volume of tackle and its inherent market phenomenon suddenly ceased. Many auctions disappeared as good tackle became hard to find and dealers began to fight tooth and nail to gain stock to sell.

For those collectors and dealers who bothered to think enough about the situation the realisation of what was happening was obvious. Examples of the reel that the collector had seen the previous twenty examples of simply disappeared. The big glut of tackle had gone and from now on good tackle would be extremely difficult to find and then only in extremely small quantities.

Those twenty examples of a certain type of reel we were talking about had probably come from a production of perhaps no more than fifty or a hundred, of which maybe only half had survived.

They had been rare examples indeed, it was just the effect of the market phenomenon we had been witnessing that made them seem not to be so. After all if one of a limited edition of a current issue of 500 prints by a famous artist can be rare today, what then is the rarity of one out of 100 reels produced in 1900 of which perhaps only 50, or even less, survived?

Let me explain some of the other factors that make a reel rare by first giving weight to my statement that maybe only half a production run of fifty or a hundred reels survived.

For example early alloys were imperfect, the quality was rough and the metal unstable and highly susceptible to corrosion, pitting and eventual breakup. Treated initially like their robust brass predecessors many were smashed or received fractured rims by the riverside.

Through time a multitude of reels have been thrown out with the rubbish by disgruntled fishing wives or disinterested inheritors; many have been ruined in the hands of offspring too young or uncaring to look after them and many have lain wet and rotting in damp basements and cellars. Some have even been accidentally dropped into rivers, lochs and seas.

Another major factor responsible for creating rarity is that some Hardy attempts at innovation were short lived.

Early reels, prototypes and transitional models were produced in extremely limited quantity. If we believe production was only fifty, a hundred or two hundred at the turn of the century then, taking the factors I have outlined into account and accepting that a number may have been exported to far flung corners of the Empire, any example of such a model today is an extremely rare item.

In collating this catalogue of my collection I hope I have succeeded in describing the items in a way that is easy for either the experienced fishing tackle collector or the person who has never before dealt with the subject to understand and that it will prove of use as a reference guide to collectors and researchers alike.

I hope that as you read through it you will find yourself enjoying and appreciating the workmanship and thought that went into these wonderful items from our piscatorial past.

Foreword by James Booth

Director of Sotheby's (Sporting Guns and Fishing Tackle) 1987

Until the end of the 19th century the development of fishing tackle was slow and comparatively unremarkable. That century saw the reel, or wynch as it was first called, come into common use and the expansion of world trade had brought with it new materials such as 'greenheart' wood for rod building, silkworm gut for lines and finally bamboo for split cane work.

However, by the last quarter of the century the angler's tackle was still relatively unsophisticated. At the risk of over simplification, rods were cumbersome, varying in length; but all of them had the same straight tapering design and were used with a choice of three forms of simple centrepin reels of wood or brass with rudimentary ratchet check mechanisms. The limitations of such tackle restricted the angler to relatively simple techniques and casting light tackle any great distance was not one of them. However although the tackle was relatively unsophisticated it would be wrong to suggest that it was crudely built; it was simply the lack of suitable materials and fresh thoughts which hindered design progress.

By the 1870's conditions were ripe for a sudden and rapid surge of innovation. The first full-length split cane rods had appeared (probably from America), lines had been refined and reels, although still simple, were built as finely and lightly as brass would allow. The new Railway networks were opening up the countryside, Victorian industry was reaching new peaks of invention and production and the rapidly growing Middle Class provided a thirsty market for anything connected with leisure and sport.

Into this fertile environment stepped the Hardy brothers who, in 1872, decided to diversify their cutlery business. Within 30 years they would become the most progressive Company in their field and eventually the most famous fishing tackle makers in the world.

Their early years were inauspicious, selling a range of tackle which was indistinguishable from that of any of their competitors. It was simple and typically Victorian and although they styled themselves 'makers' it is likely that much of it was only retailed by them.

However, in 1891 all this was to change with the introduction of their first patent fly reel. It was a brass, frameless, centrepin reel with a simple wire line guide, but its drum ran on ball bearings to reduce wear and friction and it was fitted with a ratchet-and-pawl check mechanism on which the braking tension could be adjusted. With typical Victorian self confidence they named it the 'Perfect' and it would become the most famous fly reel in the world.

Over the next twenty years the reel was radically modified and its gradual change from the all-brass to all-alloy construction perfectly illustrates the metamorphosis of the modern fly reel. There can be no greater tribute than the fact that it became the basic pattern for most fly reels and was closely copied by other makers within a few years of its appearance.

In spite of its importance the Company's success could not survive on this reel alone. In the same period they developed the Silex reel for spinning and baitcasting; again, a centrepin reel but greatly refined and fitted with sophisticated brakes and bearings to allow light tackle to be cast further than was previously possible. This reel also was modified and produced in many different forms, but in mentioning the 'Silex' and the 'Perfect' we are only looking at two out of more than 100 different reels designed since 1891 for almost every kind of coarse, game and sea fishing worldwide.

To follow Hardy's history is comparatively easy through the pages of their annual "Angler's Guides" but these show another highly important aspect of the Company's success. Obviously their equipment had to be of the highest quality and most advanced design (and these aspects have been maintained throughout) but it had to reach its market and it is clear that the Hardy's were peerless salesmen. The catalogues are both attractive and authoritative. Their pages are filled with all the paraphernalia of the sport, both practical and impractical, which was so loved by the gadget-minded Victorians and Edwardians and which was so essential to dress the 'shop window'.

It is also apparent that the Hardy's themselves were keen practical anglers, well able to appreciate the changing requirements of the day. Their pages are full of their own advice and instruction as well as testimonials from satisfied customers – two well-tried advertising techniques. They were not slow to take advice from others and some of their reels such as the Bouglé and Barton bear the names of the anglers who devised them. Even so, not all of their reels and optional extras were produced in great quantity and it is a matter of intriguing speculation as to the reasons. Did they fail to catch on or were they quickly outmoded?

However, the catalogues should not be taken at face value. Although they form comprehensive registers it is only first-hand experience that will give a true picture of the Company's work because the products were not as standard as they appeared. There are reels which cannot be found in the catalogues but which, if seldom seen, are now well known. There are common models which appear in forms which have never been illustrated. What were they? Often they turn out to be transitional models, showing a design stage between standard forms. Some are experimental models and it is the study of these anomalies which reveals the true pattern of research and development. It is the subtle changes of shape and rearrangements of mechanism which are so rewarding to the collector and the fact that so many variations exist provides endless scope for research. Has anyone yet seen an original model Perfect which exactly matched the first illustrations?
Did Hardy's actually build all the sizes of reel which they advertised?

For the Angling Historian Hardy's tackle spans the transition from ancient to modern in both tackle and technique, for the two are inextricably linked, and the Hardy brothers did more, comprehensively, than any other Company to bring angling into the 20th century. For the Collector this plethora of design and the sheer proliferation of output is a goldmine and the fact that it all came from one Company with a continuous train of thought is extraordinary.

Jess Miller has fished for 30 years and, like most collectors, his interest in the history of the sport grew out of his practical association with it. Again, as with many others, his collection began as the usual assortment of old tackle which is given to (and sometimes dumped on) a young boy with a new pastime. However his special love was salmon fishing and therefore much of this old tackle was by Hardy's.

He was fortunate that it was at a time when no value was put on second-hand tackle (few people thought of collecting it), and it was thus reasonably easy to amass what would prove to be the makings of a collection.

At an early age he developed a good appreciation of quality and it was perhaps only natural that this should steer him towards an exclusive study of Hardy's. Since then he has built, with meticulous attention to detail and quality, one of the most extensive collections of Hardy material ever gathered. In doing so he has developed a profound understanding of the Company and this Catalogue Raisonné forms one of the most comprehensive studies yet published, and the first to be based entirely on a personal collection.
.

Brass Perfect

The specification for Hardy's Perfect reel was drawn up in 1888 with a number of prototypes being made and brass Perfects were being marketed in 1890 before the reel received its patent in January 1891 under the number 612. This now world famous fly reel started its long and illustrious life as a brass model in which each part was hand made by one man, from the ivory handle to the blued spring in the check mechanism.

The Hardy catalogues of the day informed a prospective customer: 'All striking is done from the reel' i.e. that once the tension had been set for the check mechanism the angler was advised to simply hold the rod steady as a fish took and the check strength would be enough to set the hook.

Most of the early Perfects had numbers stamped beside the reel foot, however these are not a totally accurate dating guide. This practice of numbering reels appears to have ceased circa 1895 after the earliest transitional stages. The design of these early reels was changed frequently. The early, short, 'Bickerdyke' style nickel silver wire lineguard grew in stages from the two pillar version through the three and four pillar versions to eventually encircle the entire reel. After this stage the rim was changed to solid nickel silver, then to a brass rim with nickel silver pillars and finally both rim and pillars were made out of brass.

On page 152 of his book 'Fishing Tackle – A Collector's Guide' by Graham Turner there is an

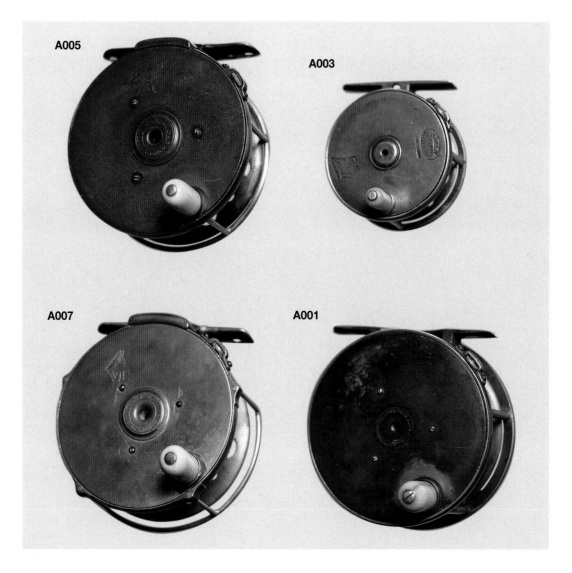

A005

A003

A007

A001

illustration of an inscribed three pillar nickel silver wire lineguard brass Perfect with the date 1890 in the inscription. A number of dated inscriptions on brass Perfects have been seen and these help as markers of the Perfect's progression, but only if the inscription date coincides with the year of manufacture which, for a number of reasons, it may not.

Two very early two pillar lineguard brass Perfects have been seen that had iron lineguards, both rusted. From every detail on these reels, one with a solid, unperforated drum, I am sure they predate the nickel silver wire lineguard models that would quickly have replaced them and they are from 1890.

Through our collective experience of the numbering, the lineguard progression, other changes in the model and research by John Drewett in his superb book 'Hardy Brothers – The Masters, the Men and their Reels' and by myself and others we are able to date the Brass Perfect's early progression reasonably accurately.

The final full brass reel case with the rim in brass was first catalogued in 1896 and throughout this period brass Perfects were being offered in ¼" steps from 2¼" to 5¼" with a giant 6" weighing 46 ounces and a

special 2⅝" dry fly model, the 'Houghton' reel, included in the range.

Early Perfects had 'open' ball races within their mechanisms whereby if the reel were tilted when opened the brass or phosphor bronze ball bearings could fall out. These ball races were soon altered to being 'closed' around the turn of the century. The hand trademark was 'shaded' on some of the early Hardy reels but although this shows that the reel is early it does not help us accurately date reels.

Other dating guides are the ivory handles on the earliest Perfects as these were changed to those of man made 'ivorine' circa 1895.

Tip: Never test a reel handle to see whether it is ivory or ivorine by trying to force something into it to see if it is 'soft' – you will devalue the reel (also never, ever polish a brass reel – Tips on Collecting page 90). One easy test for ivorine is to rub the handle vigorously with a piece of cloth or clothing until warmth is generated, if you can smell anything from the handle then it is ivorine. A second test is that due to its manufacture ivorine has uniform straight lines running through it, most often along the length of the handle, which ivory does not and ivory has a 'circular' graining within it, which ivorine does not.

A005 ***** A 4" Brass Perfect with ivory handle, hand trademark and circular 612 patent stamp in centre of face. Straight foot pierced five times and stamped 256. Dished drum with large and small perforations with large central well. Four holes in drum core. Transitional model with continuous nickel silver wire lineguard as back rim attached to face and foot by five nickel silver bridges. Strapped tension screw. Brass ball bearings in open ball race. Retaining most finish. In leather case. Excellent. Circa 1893.

A007 ***** A 4" Brass Perfect with replacement ivory handle, hand trademark, circular 612 patent stamp in centre of face. Straight foot pierced five times and stamped 211 and 18761. Dished drum with large and small perforations and large central well. Multi-perforated drum core. Two thirds nickel silver wire lineguard attached to face by four nickel silver bridges into raised pillars. Strapped tension screw. Brass ball bearings in open ball race. Overall finish worn, slightly scratched on face. In leather case. Good. Circa 1893.

A003 **** A 2¾" Brass Perfect with ivorine handle, hand trademark and enclosed oval Hardy logo. Straight foot pierced five times, the bridge pierced twice. Dished drum with large and small perforations. Strapped tension screw. Brass ball bearings in open ball race. Overall finish worn. Good. Circa 1898.

A001 **** A 4" Brass Perfect with ivory handle, shaded hand trademark and circular 612 patent stamp in centre of face. Waisted foot pierced twice, drum with large and small perforations. Transitional model with large central well in dished drum back and brass back rim with round brass bridges showing through. Strapped tension screw. Brass ball bearings in open ball race. Retaining most original finish. In leather case. Good. Circa 1895.

A002 ***** A 4½" Brass Perfect with ivory handle and shaded hand trademark opposite unusual ¾" circular stamp with Hardy name and 612 patent numbers near edge of face. Waisted foot pierced twice. Dished drum with large central well and large and small perforations. Five holes in drum core. Transitional model with solid nickel silver back rim joined to face by four slim round nickel silver bridges. Strapped tension screw. Brass ball bearings in open ball race. Retaining most finish. In leather case. Excellent. Circa 1894.

A009 ***** A 3½" Brass Perfect with ivory handle, hand trademark, enclosed oval logo and circular 612 patent stamp in centre of face. Dished drum with large and small perforations and large central well. Multi-perforated drum core. Straight foot pierced three times and stamped 22. Single section 'Bickerdyke' nickel silver wire lineguard covering one quarter of the reel's circumference joined to two raised pillars beside face. The brass piece of one pillar is further shaped to incorporate the strap over the tension screw. Brass ball bearings in open ball race. One small plate screw missing from face. Retaining most finish. In leather case. Superb. Circa 1891.

A004 **** A 2½" Brass Perfect with ivorine handle, shaded hand trademark and enclosed oval logo. Waisted foot, dished drum with large and small perforations. Transitional model with three round nickel silver bridges joining brass back rim to face. Strapped tension screw. Brass ball bearings in open ball race. Overall finish worn. Good. Circa 1895.

A008 ***** A 4" Brass Perfect with ivory handle, hand trademark and circular 612 patent stamp in centre of face. Straight foot pierced three times and stamped 35. Dished drum with large and small perforations and central well. Long single section nickel silver wire 'Bickerdyke' lineguard covering one third of circumference and joined to two raised pillars on rim. Multi-perforated drum core. Strapped tension screw. Brass ball bearings in open ball race. Check spring broken under tension device which was made too tight for the spring to pass under without wearing severely. Retaining most finish. In leather case. Superb. Circa 1890.

A018 ***** A 2½" Brass Perfect with tapered ivorine handle, hand trademark and circular 612 patent stamp in centre of face. Straight foot pierced three times and stamped 52. dished drum with large and small perforations, large well and multi-perforated drum core. One third single section nickel silver 'Bickerdyke' line guide joined to two raised pillars beside face. Strapped tension screw and brass ball bearings in open ball race (a few missing). One small plate screw missing from face. Worn finish. Good. Circa 1891.

A010 ***** A 4¼" Brass Perfect with ivory handle, hand trademark, enclosed oval logo and 'Hardy's Pat.Perfect Reel' stamped on face. Transitional model with special optional alloy drum, dished with large and small perforations and 14 cusps. Straight foot pierced seven times. Turk's head locking nut over tension screw. Brass ball bearings in open ball race. Overall finish worn. In leather case. Good. Circa 1898.

A006 ***** A 3¾" Brass Perfect with ivory handle, hand trademark, circular 612 patent stamp in centre of face and the initials J W M scroll engraved on face. Straight foot pierced three times and stamped 124. Dished drum with large and small perforations and large central well. Multi-perforated drum core. Transitional model with continuous nickel silver wire lineguard as back rim attached to face by three nickel silver bridges into raised pillars and to foot by a fourth nickel silver bridge. Strapped tension screw. Brass ball bearings in open ball race. Retaining good finish with dark brown patina. In leather case. Excellent. Circa 1892.

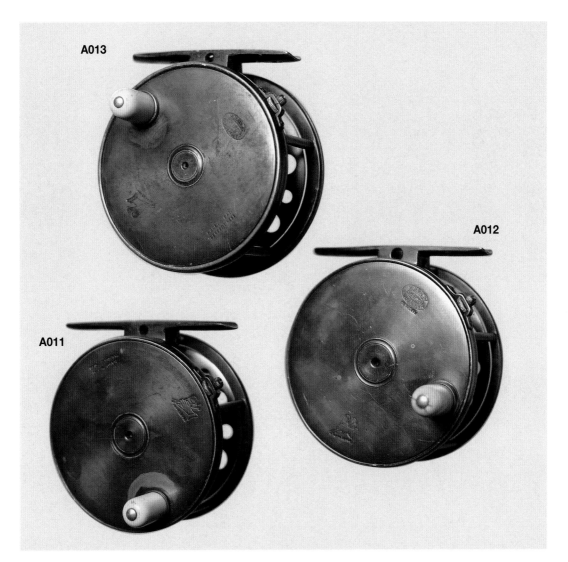

A013 *** A 4½" Brass Perfect with ivorine handle, hand trademark, enclosed oval logo and 'Hardy's Pat.Perfect Reel' stamped on face. Straight foot pierced seven times. Dished drum with large and small perforations. Turk's head locking nut over tension screw. Brass ball bearings in open ball race. Retaining most finish with honest wear. Excellent. Circa 1898.

A011 **** A 4" Brass Perfect with ivorine handle, hand trademark, enclosed oval logo and 'Hardy's Pat.Perfect Reel' stamped on face. Straight foot pierced seven times. Dished drum with large and small perforations. Turk's head locking nut over tension screw. Brass ball bearings in open ball race. Retaining most finish with honest wear. In leather case. Superb. Circa 1898.

A012 *** A 4¼" Brass Perfect with ivory handle, hand trademark and enclosed oval logo on face. Straight foot pierced five times. Dished drum with large and small perforations. Turk's head locking nut over tension screw. Brass ball bearings in open ball race. Retaining most finish. In leather case. Excellent. Circa 1898.

A016

A016 ***** A 5" Brass Perfect with ivory handle, hand trademark, enclosed oval logo and waisted foot. Dished drum with large and small perforations. Strapped tension screw. Transitional model with brass back rim joined to face by four nickel silver pillars showing through the back rim. Brass ball bearings in open ball race. Retaining most finish. In leather case. Excellent. Circa 1894.

A020

A021

A015 **** A 4¾" Brass Perfect with ivorine handle, hand trademark and 'Hardy's Pat.Perfect Reel' stamped on face. Straight foot pierced seven times. Dished drum with large and small perforations. Turk's head locking nut over tension screw. Brass ball bearings in enclosed ball race. Finish worn but good. In leather case. Very good. Circa 1898.

A017 ***** A 3" Brass Perfect with ivory handle, hand trademark and raised circular 612 patent stamp in centre of face. Waisted foot, dished drum with large and small perforations and large well. Strapped tension screw. Transitional model with brass back rim joined to face by three nickel silver pillars showing through back rim. Multi-perforated drum core. Brass ball bearings in open ball race. Good finish with honest wear. Very Good. Circa 1893.

A019 **** A 2½" Brass Perfect with ivorine handle, hand trademark, enclosed oval logo and 'Hardy's Pat.Perfect Reel' stamped on face. Waisted foot pierced twice. Dished drum with large and small perforations. Brass ball bearings in open ball race. Worn finish. One scratch on face and one bridge severely cut into by line. Good. Circa 1896.

A014 *** A 4½" Brass Perfect with ivorine handle, hand trademark, enclosed oval logo and 'Hardy's Pat.Perfect Reel' stamped on face. Straight foot pierced five times. Dished drum with large and small perforations. Turk's head locking nut over tension screw. Brass ball bearings in open ball race (a few missing). Retaining most original silvery bronzing finish. In leather case. Superb. Circa 1898.

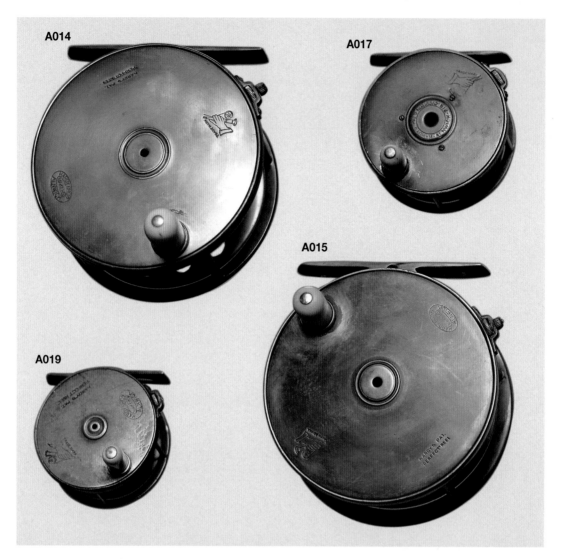

A020 ***** A 2¾" Brass Perfect with ivory handle, hand trademark and circular 612 patent stamp in centre of face. Waisted foot, dished drum with large and small perforations, large well, multi-perforated drum core. Transitional model with brass back rim joined to face by three nickel silver pillars showing through the back rim. Strapped tension screw. Brass ball bearings in open ball race. Retaining most original finish. Superb. Circa 1894.

A021 ***** A 3½" Brass Perfect with ivory handle, hand trademark, enclosed oval logo and circular 612 patent stamp in centre of face. Dished drum with large and small perforations and large central well. Multi-perforated drum core. Straight foot pierced three times and stamped 21. Single section 'Bickerdyke' nickel silver wire lineguard covering one quarter of the reel's circumference joined to two raised pillars beside face. Strapped tension screw. Brass ball bearings in open ball race. Retaining most finish. Superb. Circa 1891.

B107 ***** A 4¼" Brass Faced Perfect with ivorine handle, hand trademark and straightline logos. Brass foot with central hole, unique solid drum of ebonite with large internal central brass bush and 4 cusps, turk's head locking nut over tension device, 1903 brass framed lineguard. Late 1896 Check with four screw block. Retaining most finish. In leather case. Superb. Circa 1904.

B105 *** A 4¾" Brass Faced Perfect with ivorine handle, hand trademark and straightline logos. Brass foot with central hole, drum with 8 cusps, turk's head locking nut over tension screw, 1903 brass framed lineguard. 1906 Check. Retaining most finish. Excellent. 1906-1909.

B101 **** A 4" Brass Faced Perfect with ivorine handle, hand trademark, enclosed oval and straightline logos. Unique model with fixed Check (no tension screw fitted). Brass foot replacing original alloy foot, drum with 8 cusps, waisted bridges. Retaining most finish. In leather case. Very Good. Circa 1901.

Section B
Brass Faced Perfect

Before 1900 Hardy's had been developing the use of alloy in reel making having found they could make their heavy brass reels considerably lighter and fishing less onerous for the angler. However their early attempts at convincing anglers that alloy was the way forward were frowned upon as the angling public had been comfortable with brass reels for a very long time. To the Victorian angler alloy did not look strong enough to be used for reel making.

But Hardy's realised the value of alloy to the angling world and began a system of slowly 'educating' their customers to its use. First they offered the final model of the Brass Perfect with a special optional alloy drum. Of these I have only seen one (numbered 138) and it must have been a thankless task trying to convince a wary public to buy them. Then they made the Perfect with a case of alloy but a face of brass. This looked much more acceptable and through the turn of the century and up to about 1912 a Brass Faced Perfect became the reel to fish with.

Although we cannot be precise as to the exact date of the start of the Brass Faced Perfects some figures written by J.J.Hardy in his 1899 catalogue record the changes in weight with the wide drum salmon reels getting lighter as the case was changed to alloy and the contracted reels getting heavier as the face was changed back to brass to make the reel sell better. In 1906 the checking mechanism was changed by putting in a larger brass piece, held by four screws, to house the pawl.
Many Brass Faced Perfects had a fairly delicate integral alloy foot which tended to break and it was commonplace for Hardy's to replace it in brass. Experimentation was great throughout this period and a number of unique reels were made.

B102 *** A 4" Brass Faced Perfect with ivorine handle, hand trademark, enclosed oval and straightline logos. Unique model with fixed Check (no tension screw fitted). Brass foot replacing original alloy foot, drum with 8 cusps, waisted bridges. Retaining most finish. In leather case. Very Good. Circa 1901.

B103 **** A 4¼" Brass Faced Perfect with ivorine handle, hand trademark, open oval and straightline logos. Integral alloy foot with central hole, solid unperforated drum with 4 cusps, turk's head locking nut over tension screw. 1896 Check. Retaining most finish. In leather case. Excellent. Circa 1900.

B104 **** A 4½" Brass Faced Perfect with ivorine handle, hand trademark and straightline logo. The face with unusual 1" nickel silver medallion in centre of face stamped 'Hardy's Patent Alnwick'. Neatly engraved W.H.S.Cutler 2. Brass foot, drum with 4 cusps, turk's head locking nut over tension screw. 1903 brass framed lineguard. 1906 Check. Retaining most finish. Very good. 1906-1909.

B106 ***** A 5" Brass Faced Perfect with ivorine handle, hand trademark, enclosed oval and straightline logos. Brass foot replacing original alloy foot, drum with large and small perforations, turk's head locking nut over tension screw. Early 1896 Check with S-spring bearing on head of pawl. Retaining most finish. Excellent. Circa 1900.

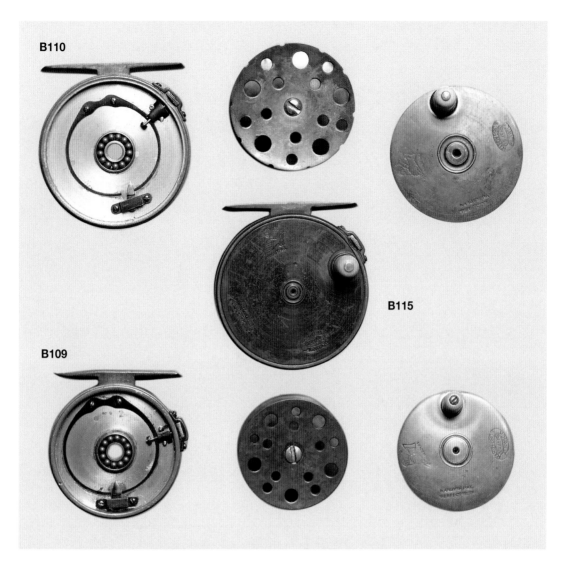

B109 ***** A 2⅝" Brass Faced Perfect (the 'Houghton' dry fly reel) with ivorine handle, hand trademark, enclosed oval and straightline logos. Brass foot. Transitional model with brass face and drum, the drum having large and small perforations, and alloy case. Strapped tension screw. 1896 Check. A few line grooves in rim. In non-Hardy leather case with broken strap. Very Good. Circa 1900.

B110 ***** A 3" Brass Faced Perfect with ivorine handle, hand trademark, enclosed oval and straightline logos. Brass foot. Transitional model with brass face and drum, the drum having large and small perforations and 10 cusps. Alloy case with waisted bridges. 1896 Check. Retaining most finish. In leather case. Excellent. Circa 1900.

B115 **** A 3⅛" Brass Faced Contracted Perfect with ivorine handle on fluted cup, hand trademark, enclosed oval and straightline logos. Brass foot, drum with 4 cusps, strapped tension screw, 1896 Check. Retaining most finish. Excellent. 1900-1902.

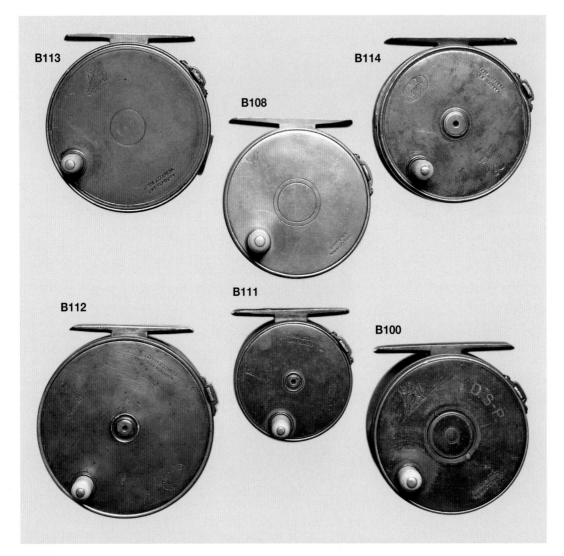

B100 *** A 3½" Brass Faced Perfect with ivorine handle, hand trademark and straightline logo. Brass foot with central hole. Prominently knurled rim edges, strapped tension screw. 1896 Check. Face with 1" turned groove in centre and initials D S-P neatly engraved. Very Good. Circa 1901.

B108 *** A 3¼" Brass Faced Perfect with ivorine handle, hand trademark and straightline logos. Brass foot (slightly shortened) with central hole, drum with 4 cusps, strapped tension screw, knurled rims. 1896 Check. Polished face and drum. Good. 1900-1904.

B111 *** A 2⅝" Brass Faced Perfect – The 'Houghton' Dry Fly Reel – with ivorine handle in fluted cup, hand trademark, enclosed oval and straightline logos. Brass foot, strapped tension screw. 1896 Check. Retaining most finish. Excellent. 1900-1906.

B112 **** A 3⅞" Brass Faced Contracted Perfect with ivorine handle on fluted cup, hand trademark, enclosed oval logo (minus the central word 'Makers') and straightline logo. Brass foot, drum with 4 cusps. 1896 Check. Finish worn. In leather case. Fair. 1900-1902.

B113 **** A 3⅝" Brass Faced Contracted Perfect with ivorine handle on fluted cup, hand trademark and straightline logo. Brass foot, drum with 4 cusps, strapped tension screw, red agate lineguard. 1896 Check with S-spring on pawl head. Some pitting around back rim. In leather case. Good. 1900-1902.

B114 **** A 3⅜" Brass Faced Contracted Perfect with ivorine handle on fluted cup, hand trademark, enclosed oval and straightline logos. Brass foot, drum with 7 cusps, strapped tension screw, waisted bridges. 1896 Check. Finish worn. In leather case. Fair. 1900-1902.

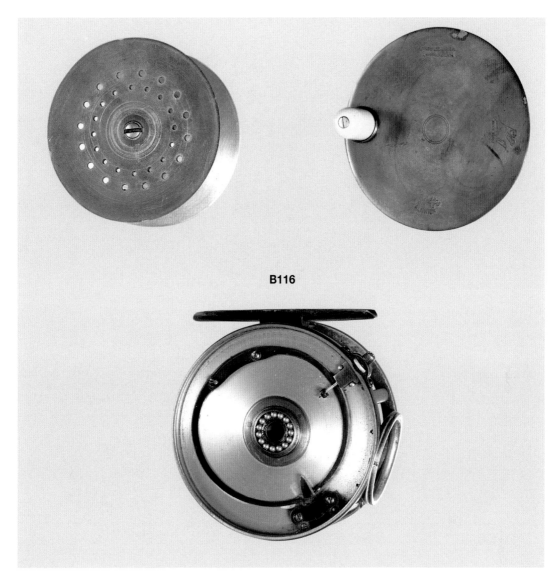

B116

B116 *** A 4¼" Brass Faced Perfect with ivorine handle, hand trademark, open oval and straightline logos. Brass foot, drum with 4 cusps, turk's head locking nut over tension screw. 1903 brass framed lineguard. Late 1906 Check. Retaining most finish. Excellent. Circa 1906.

B117

B117 *** A 4¼" Brass Faced Perfect with ivorine handle, hand trademark and straightline logos. Brass foot, drum with 4 cusps, turk's head locking nut over tension screw. 1903 brass framed lineguard. 1906 Check. Mint, in non-Hardy leather case. Superb. Circa 1906.

Alloy Perfect

Alloy Perfects were started in the late 1890's but their sales struggled until the demise of the Brass Faced Perfect towards 1912. As soon as they could Hardy's brought their Perfect reels to full alloy production in a great range of sizes.

Hand trademarks appearing on alloy reels are rare and even more so on wide drum Perfects.

White handled alloy Perfects date up to about 1920.

Those with a notched brass foot are post 1928.

The Duplicated Mk II Check ran from about 1920.

The 'straightline' logo on alloy reels changed to the modern version from around 1950 onwards.

The alloy Perfects span a great number of years and consequently their total production was vast. However there are early examples and experimental 'one off' models that are extremely rare.

Alloy Perfects formed the bulk of Hardy's reel success and were exported to the farthest corners of the Empire. It took little time for them to be found being used in every form of freshwater game fishing all over the world.

The variations are enormous and so I always concentrate on rare items such as those with hand trademarks, silent checks or specialist sizes, etc.

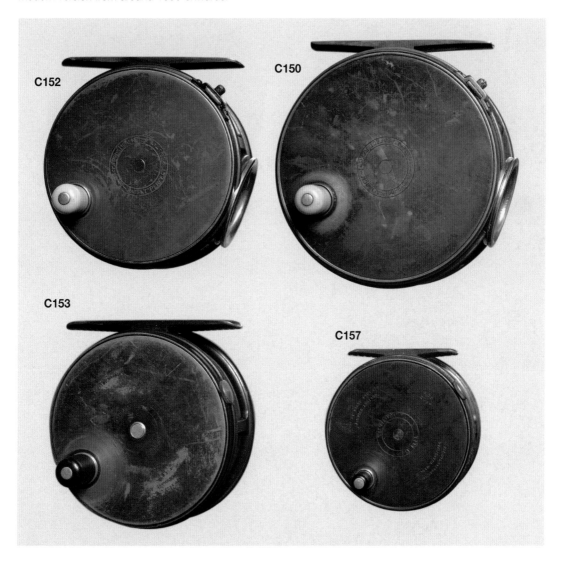

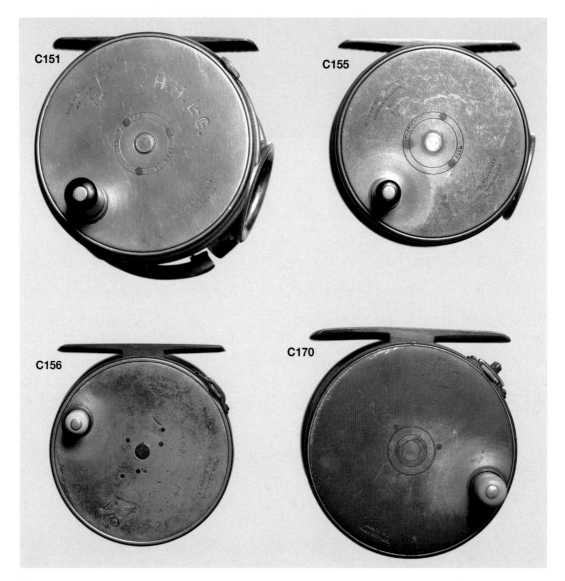

C150 **** A 5" Alloy Perfect with fat ivorine handle, brass foot (one end slightly shortened), drum with 4 cusps, turks head locking nut over tension screw. 1903 brass framed lineguard. 1906 check. Retaining most finish. Excellent. 1906-1908.

C151 **** A 4¼" Alloy Perfect with fat black handle, notched brass foot, drum with turned rim for fitted optional auxiliary brass rim brake (available from 1924 until World War II).
The face neatly engraved with the initials H.H.L-G (Captain Henry Herbert Liddell-Grainger, Scots Guards of Ayton Castle, Eyemouth, Berwickshire 1886-1935). Duplicated Mk II Check and revolving patent nickel silver lineguard. Worn Finish. Very good. Circa 1930.

C152 ** A 4¼" Alloy Perfect with fat ivorine handle, brass foot, turk's head locking nut over tension screw, revolving patent nickel silver lineguard. 1912 Check. Retaining most finish. In contemporary Hardy box. Excellent. 1912-1917.

C153 ***** An Alloy Perfect stamped 4¼" which actually measures 4⅛", with fat black handle, notched brass foot and Duplicated Mk II Check. This unique reel has a 'contracted' drum measuring 1" between the plates as against 1¼" on a normal 4¼" reel. Retaining most finish with honest wear. In leather case. Very good. 1930's.

C154 **** A 4" Alloy Perfect with fat ivorine handle, brass foot, strapped tension screw and Silent Check. Retaining most finish. In leather case. Very good. 1920's.

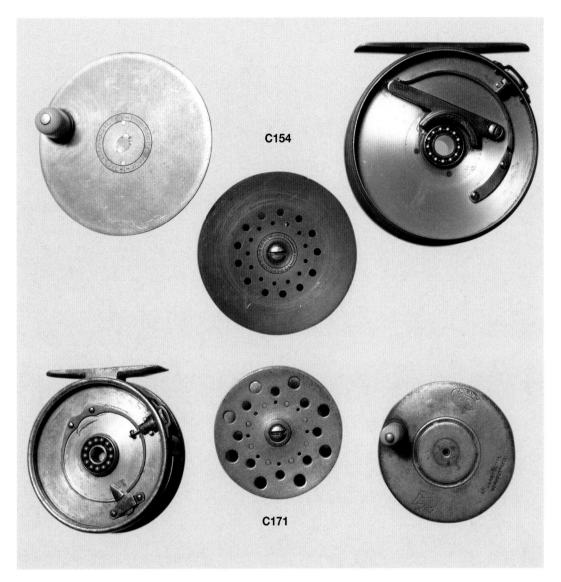

C154

C171

C155 **** A 3¾" Alloy Perfect with slim black handle, notched brass foot and revolving patent nickel silver lineguard. Stamped 'Duplicated Mk II' and having Silent Check bearing patent No.196736. Lightly worn finish. Very good. 1930's.

C156 ***** A 3½" Alloy Perfect with slim ivorine handle on fluted cup, hand trademark, open oval and straightline logos. Brass foot, strapped tension screw. 1896 Check. Very good condition for such an early reel. Circa 1899.

C157 ** A 3¼" Alloy Perfect with slim black handle and notched brass foot. Duplicated Mk II Check. Retaining most finish. Superb. 1930's.

C170 ***** A 4" Alloy Perfect with fat ivorine handle, hand trademark and straightline logos. Brass foot, drum with 4 cusps and turk's head locking nut over tension screw. 1906 Check. Retaining most finish with some honest wear. Very good. Circa 1906.

C171 ***** A 3⅛" Alloy Contracted Perfect with ivorine handle, hand trademark, enclosed oval and straightline logos. Important transitional reel with alloy foot, drum caged and dished rising to central brass bush and with large and small perforations. Brass ball bearings in open ball race. Flat bridges each with two holes, raised and incised 1⁷⁄₁₆" central feature on face and strapped tension screw. 1896 Check. Finish worn with light overall pitting. Very good. Circa 1899.

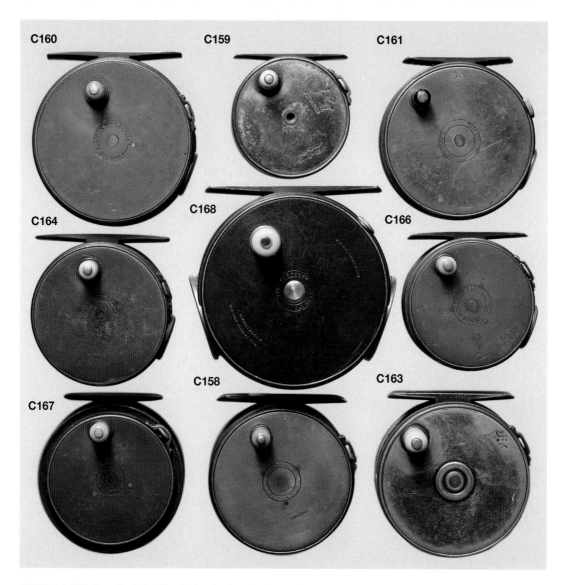

C158 ** A 3¼" Alloy Perfect with slim ivorine handle, brass foot and strapped tension screw. 1912 Check. Worn finish with lightly worn finish on face. In leather case. Very good. 1912-1917.

C159 **** A 2⅝" Alloy Perfect with slim ivorine handle on fluted cup, hand trademark, open oval and straightline logos with navel centre to face. Brass foot, strapped tension screw, drum with 4 cusps and 1896 Check. Retaining most finish with honest wear. Very good. 1900-1902.

C160 ** A 3⅝" Alloy Contracted Perfect with slim ivorine handle, brass foot, strapped tension screw and red agate lineguard. 1896 Check. Retaining most finish. Very good. 1902-1910.

C161 **** A 3⅜" Alloy Contracted Perfect with slim black handle, notched brass foot and white agate lineguard. Stamped Duplicated Mk II but has Silent Check patent No.196736. Retaining most finish. Very good. 1930's.

C162 * A 3⅜" Alloy Contracted Perfect with slim ivorine handle, brass foot, drum with 4 cusps and Mk 1 Check. Retaining most finish. In leather case. Excellent. Circa 1920.

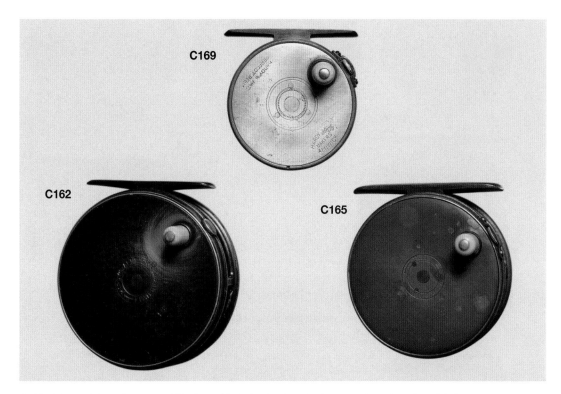

C163 **** A 3⅜" Alloy Contracted Perfect with fat ivorine handle, hand trademark and straightline logos. Alloy foot with central hole, strapped tension screw, prominently knurled rims, attractively raised and incised central feature on face. 1896 Check. Lightly worn finish. In leather case. Good. 1896-1898.

C164 *** A 3⅛" Alloy Contracted Perfect with slim ivorine handle, brass foot, strapped tension screw, drum with 4 cusps and red agate line guide. 1896 Check. Retaining most finish. In leather case. Excellent. 1902-1910.

C165 * A 3⅛" Alloy Contracted Perfect with slim ivorine handle, brass foot, strapped tension screw, and 1912 Check. Honest wear. In leather case. Good. 1912-1917.

C166 *** A 2⅞" Alloy Contracted Perfect with slim ivorine handle, brass foot, strapped tension screw, drum with 4 cusps, red agate lineguard and 1896 Check. Honest wear. Very good. Circa 1910.

C167 *** A 3¼" Alloy Special Perfect with slim ivorine handle, brass foot (slightly shortened), raised face with strapped tension screw to side and 1906 Check. Retaining most finish. Excellent. Circa 1910.

C168 ***** A 4¼" Alloy Perfect with fat ivorine handle, alloy foot and Duplicated Mk II Check. The reel is fitted with dual line guides enabling it to be used either left or right handed. Retaining most finish. Excellent. Early 1920's.

C169 **** A 2½" Alloy Perfect with ivorine handle on fluted cup, open oval and straightline logos, brass foot and strapped tension screw. 1896 Check. Face has been polished. Good. Circa 1905.

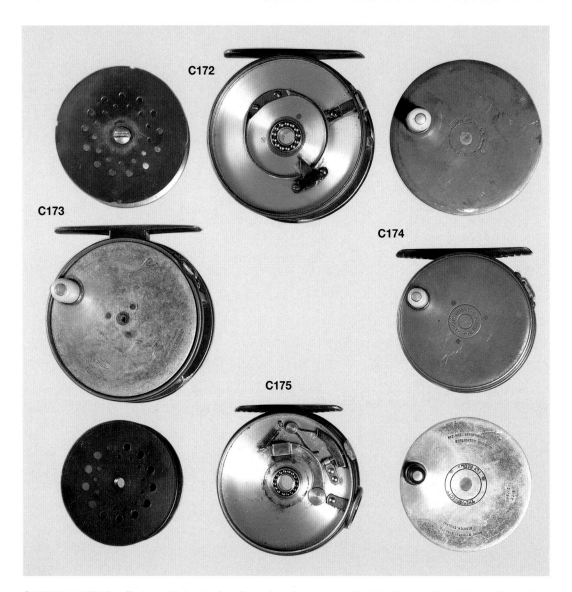

C172 *** A 3½" Alloy Perfect with ivorine handle and central circular 'Hardy's Alnwick Patent' logo. Brass foot, strapped tension screw, drum with 4 cusps. 1906 Check with Walter Dingley's 'D' stamp. Mint. Superb. Circa 1906.

C173 ***** A 3½" Alloy Perfect with ivorine handle, hand trademark, open oval and straightline logos. Integral alloy foot with central hole, drum with 4 cusps and strapped tension screw. 1896 Check. Finish with honest wear. Very good. Circa 1900.

C174 **** A 3" Alloy Perfect with ivorine handle and central circular 'Hardy's Patent Alnwick' logo. Replacement notched brass foot, strapped tension screw, drum with 4 cusps. 1896 Check. Finish with honest wear. Very good. Circa 1904.

C175 **** A 3⅛" Alloy Contracted Perfect with slim black handle, notched brass foot and white agate lineguard. Stamped Duplicated Mk II but has Silent Check Patent No.196736. Worn finish. In leather case. Very good. 1930's.

C177 ***** A 3⅛" Alloy Contracted Perfect (similar model type to C171) with ivorine handle, hand trademark, enclosed oval and straightline logos. Important transitional reel with replacement brass foot, slightly dished drum with large and small perforations. No ball race – only raised, cone shaped brass bush. Flat bridges each with two holes. Raised and incised 1⅜ central feature on face. Fixed 1896 Check – No tension adjuster. Overall finish worn but retaining much finish on face and backplate. Very good. Circa 1899.

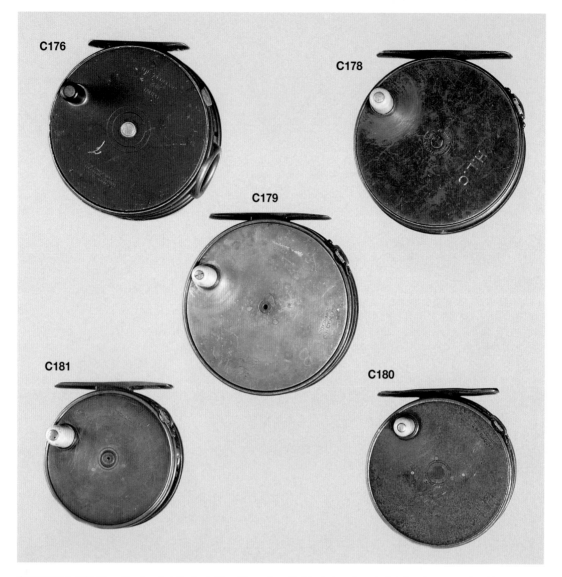

C176 **** A 3⅞" Alloy Contracted Perfect, The "Taupo", with black handle, straightline logo, notched brass foot, nickel silver lineguard and Duplicated Mk II Check. finish with honest wear and two scratches on faceplate. Good. 1950's.

C178 *** A 3⅞" Alloy Contracted Perfect with ivorine handle and central circular 'Hardy's Patent Alnwick' logo. Brass foot and strapped tension screw. 1896 Check. The face engraved 'H.L.C.' Retaining most finish. Excellent Circa 1905.

C179 **** A 3⅞" Alloy contracted Perfect with ivorine handle on fluted cup, hand trademark, open oval and straightline logos, brass foot and strapped tension screw. 1896 Check. Finish worn on face but overall good. Very good. Circa 1898.

C180 **** A 3⅜" Alloy Contracted Perfect with ivorine handle on fluted cup, hand trademark and straightline logo. Brass foot with central hole and strapped tension screw. 1896 Check. Honest wear. Very good. Circa 1898.

C181 **** A 3⅛" Alloy Contracted Perfect with ivorine handle, hand trademark and straightline logos. Brass foot and strapped tension screw. 1896 Check. Honest wear. Circa 1898.

Bouglé

In 1903 Hardy's introduced a Perfect variant made to the specification of one M.Bouglé. It seems that M.Bouglé wanted an extremely lightweight trout reel capable of carrying a relatively large amount of line. The average weight of 4¼ ozs. for the Bouglé made it lighter than a Perfect of smaller diameter. With its offset pillars and often highly polished appearance the Bouglé remains a source of great interest to keen collectors.

The Bouglé was made from 1903 until World War II in two sizes – 3" and 3¾".

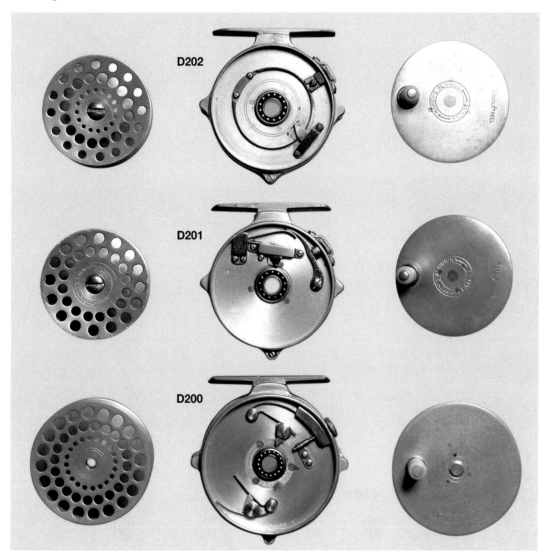

D200 **** A 3¼" Bouglé dry fly reel with ivorine handle, brass foot, 3 offset pillars (one roller opposite foot) and multi-perforated drum. Duplicated Mk II Check. Retaining original silvery finish throughout. Superb. Circa 1925.

D201 **** A 3" Bouglé dry fly reel with ivorine handle, nickel plated brass foot, 3 offset pillars (one roller opposite foot), multi-perforated drum and strapped tension screw. The face stamped 'Bouglé' reel. Nickel plated heavy duty 1912 Check. Retaining original silvery finish throughout. Superb. 1912-1920.

D202 **** A 3" Bouglé dry fly reel with ivorine handle, brass foot, 3 offset pillars (one roller opposite foot), multi-perforated drum and strapped tension screw. The face stamped 'Bouglé' reel. 1906 Check. Honest wear. Excellent. Circa 1906.

Section E
Brass

The arrival of brass platewind reels, including the Brass Perfect, heralded the end of the old brass reels, previously known as wynches. These old collar and spike fitting wynches, in use for centuries, were suddenly usurped by their modern, more useful counterparts.

From around the end of the 1870's Hardy's were selling crankwind reels, where the handle was on the end of a crank arm rather than fixed to the reel's faceplate, in sizes 1¼", 1½", 1¾", 2", 2¼", 2½", 2¾" and 3". In 1891 the range was increased with sizes 3¼", 3½", 3¾", 4", 4¼" and 4½". Some of these reels were made with the crank arm inside a raised 'anti-foul' outer rim, to prevent the line from fouling underneath the crank handle. Examples have been seen (E253) that were nickel plated before being stamped and some of these have raised pillars, standing outside the rim of the reel. The crankwind reels continued until 1901.

From around 1889 through the early Perfect years Hardy's were also selling a range of plain brass platewind reels, referred to by collectors as 'Birmingham' reels after the city that was the centre of brass manufacture in England. Offered initially in sizes 2¼", 2½", 2¾", 3", 3½", 4", 4½" and 5" the range was cut down to the 2¼", 2½", 2¾" and 3" sizes from 1910 until it ended around 1920. Due to their solid construction these reels have survived well down the years.

Brass and Ebonite (an early form of plastic) reels with nickel silver rims were offered from 1886 with a brass face and ebonite backplate. These came in sizes 2¼", 2½", 3", 3½", 4", 4½" and 5" with intermediate sizes 3¼", 3¾", 4¼" and 4¾" being added from 1888 and the range finished in 1897.

From 1884 Hardy's also produced their Special Pattern fly reel made from 'Hercules' metal, brass beaten until it became exceptionally hard. With their distinctive raised faceplates they were lighter than the Birmingham or Brass & Ebonite reels and in 1886 were available in 2¼", 2½", 4" and 4½" sizes with the 2¼" being deleted from the catalogue in 1888.
In that year a 3" and 3½" size were added.
In 1894 sizes 2⅝", 3¼", 3¾" and 4¼" were added.
Pre-1900 a Hercules was offered in alloy as opposed to brass and these are extremely rare.
The Hercules ended in 1903.

There is no doubt that these early brass reels have a unique place in the history of the development of Hardy's. Some of the actual measurements below do not correlate with those offered in Hardy's catalogues and would have been rounded to the nearest published size when offered for sale.

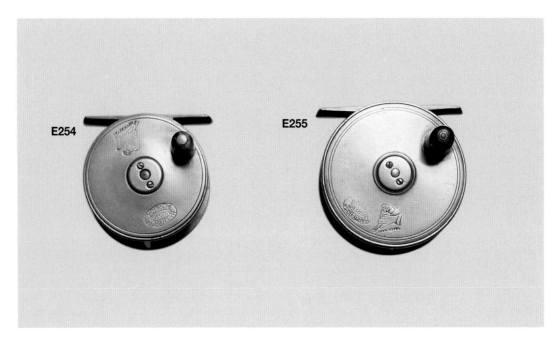

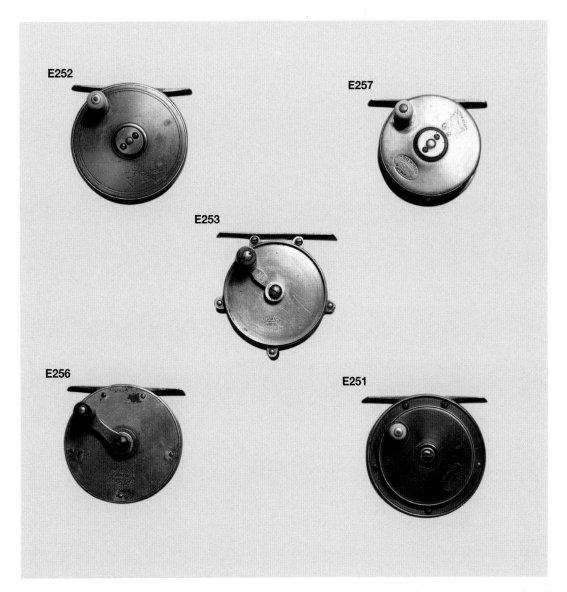

E252

E257

E253

E256

E251

E250 **** A 3¾" crankwind brass fly reel with tapered ebony handle on the end of a waisted crank arm, hand trademark, enclosed oval logo and brass foot (lightly filed). Retaining most finish. Very good. 1890's.

E251 **** A 2½" crankwind brass fly reel with tapered ebony handle on the end of a waisted crank arm, enclosed oval logo and brass foot. Finish worn. Good. 1890's.

E252 ** A 2¼" platewind brass 'Birmingham' reel with ivorine handle, shaded hand trademark, enclosed oval logo and brass foot. Retaining most finish. Excellent. 1890's.

E253 ***** A unique 2¼" crankwind nickel plated brass fly reel with bone handle on shaped crank arm set inside an anti-foul rim. Enclosed oval logo on face. Five raised pillars of which two support the foot which is steel pinned. The backplate with beautifully scrolled initials M.J.B. Retaining most finish. Superb. 1880's.

E254 * A 2⅜" platewind brass 'Birmingham' reel with tapered horn handle, hand trademark, enclosed oval logo and brass foot. The reel has been polished. Good. 1890's.

E255 * A 2¾" platewind brass 'Birmingham' reel with tapered ebony handle, hand trademark, enclosed oval logo and brass foot. The reel has been polished. Good. 1890's.

E256 *** A 2⅝" platewind brass Special Pattern fly reel with ivorine handle on fluted cup on raised face, enclosed oval logo and brass foot. Retaining most finish. Very good. 1890's.

E257 *** A 2½" platewind Brass and Ebonite fly reel with ivorine handle, hand trademark, enclosed oval logo, brass faceplate, ebonite backplate, nickel silver rims and brass foot. Retaining most finish. Superb. 1890's.

E258 ** A 2¾" platewind brass Special Pattern fly reel with ivorine handle on fluted cup on raised face, hand trademark, open oval logo and brass foot. Retaining most finish. Excellent. Circa 1890.

E259 * A 4¼" platewind brass 'Birmingham' reel with ivorine handle, hand trademark, enclosed oval logo and brass foot. Retaining most finish. In non-Hardy leather case with Sir Basil Montgomery's name written on it in ink. Excellent. 1890's.

E260 *** A 5" brass and ebonite fly reel with tapered ebony handle, enclosed oval logo, brass faceplate, ebonite backplate, nickel silver rims and brass foot. Retaining most finish. Very good. Circa 1890.

E261 **** A 2³⁄₁₆" Crankwind brass fly reel with tapered horn handle on curved crank arm stamped 'Hardy's Alnwick'. Brass foot. Finish worn. Good. 1890's.

E262 **** A 2½" Crankwind brass fly reel with tapered ebony handle on waisted crank arm. With enclosed oval logo and brass foot. Retaining much original lacquered finish. Excellent. 1890's.

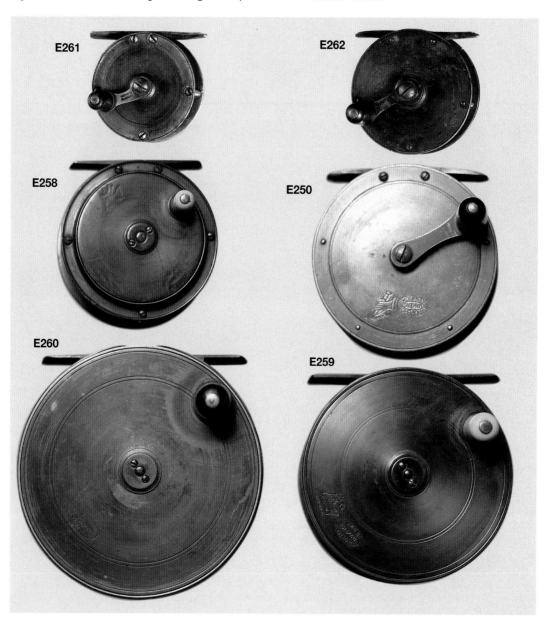

St.George

Next to the Perfect in length of production comes the St.George.

Introduced as a 3¾" model in 1911 the St.George followed a similar line of development and change to the Perfect with alterations of check mechanisms and size ranges. Its options provided a useful extension to the Hardy range as well as complementing the Perfect. The 3⅜" size appeared in 1913 and the 3" appeared in 1920.

A St.George Salmon of 4¼" arrived in 1920, but made no inroads into the successful sales of the Salmon Perfects and its production period was shortened to just four years ending in 1924.

Multiplying St.Georges appeared in 1927 and were sold in two sizes, 3⅜" and 3¾" until the start of World War II.

A Silent Check St.George was available from 1920 and a St.George Junior of 2⁹⁄₁₆" appeared in 1928.

Again there are rare St.Georges such as the Salmon, Silent, Tournament, etc., and left hand wind versions are seldom seen as with most other Hardy models.

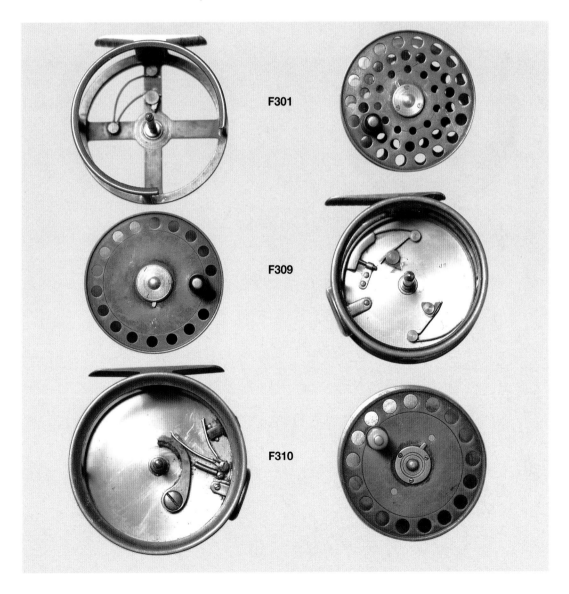

F301

F309

F310

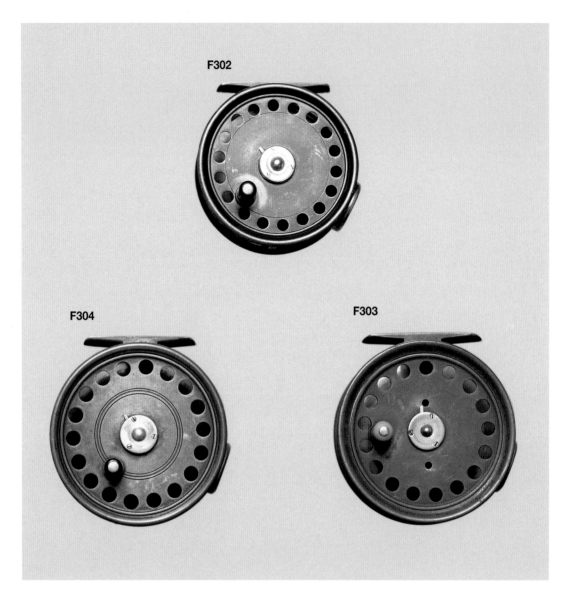

F302

F304

F303

F300 ** A 3" St.George with black handle, notched brass foot, white agate lineguard and three screw drum latch. Duplicated Mk II Check. Finish worn. Good. 1930's.

F301 ***** A 3¼" St.George Tournament fly reel, purportedly one of only three made, with black handle, notched polished alloy foot, three screw drum latch and single unadjustable check. The drum is multi-perforated both sides. The backplate is cut away leaving a supporting cross of metal ⅜" wide through which the check is clearly visible and on which is stamped 'Hardy Bros. Ltd. Makers. Alnwick. Eng.' and, neatly scratched, 'D.B. 1936'. One quarter of the front rim is broken away, probably deliberately to give finger control to the revolving drum edge. Retaining most finish. Very good. 1936.

F302 * A 3⅜" St.George with black handle, notched brass foot, white agate lineguard and three screw drum latch. Duplicated Mk II Check. Retaining most finish. Very good. 1930's.

F303 ** A 3¾" St.George with ivorine handle, brass foot, red agate lineguard, strapped tension screw and three screw drum latch. 1910 Check. Retaining most finish. Excellent. 1910-1912.

F304 * A 3¾" St.George with black handle, alloy foot, white agate lineguard and three screw drum latch. Duplicated Mk II Check. Finish lightly worn. Good. 1920's.

F305 ** A 2⁹⁄₁₆" St.George Junior with black handle, polished alloy foot, white agate lineguard and two screw drum latch. Duplicated Mk II Check. Mint. Superb. Circa 1950.

F306 * A 3" St.George with black handle, polished alloy foot, white agate lineguard and two screw drum latch. Duplicated Mk II Check. Spare drum. In leather case. Mint. Superb. Circa 1950

F307 ** A 3⅜" St.George Multiplier with black reverse tapered handle, notched brass foot, white agate lineguard, three screw drum latch and 2:1 multiplying action. Finish lightly worn. In leather case. Very good. 1930's.

F308 ** A 3¾" St.George Multiplier with black handle, notched brass foot, white agate lineguard, three screw drum latch and 2:1 multiplying action. Finish lightly worn. In leather case. Very good. 1930's.

F309 ***** A unique 3⅜" St.George with black handle. Left hand wind model with white agate lineguard and tension screw in the left hand position. The reel is fitted with a notched brass 'Barton' foot (see Section I) reversed to position the reel as far down the rod as possible. Three screw drum latch and Duplicated Mk II check. Finish lightly worn. Very good. 1940's.

F310 **** A 3¾" Silent St.George with ivorine handle, brass foot, red agate lineguard (cracked), strapped tension screw and three screw drum latch. Silent check. Finish lightly worn. Very good. Circa 1922.

F311 **** A 4¼" St.George Salmon with single black handle, brass foot, patent nickel silver lineguard and three screw drum latch. Duplicated Mk II Check. Large initials C.M. neatly engraved on face. Finish slightly worn. Very good. Circa 1920.

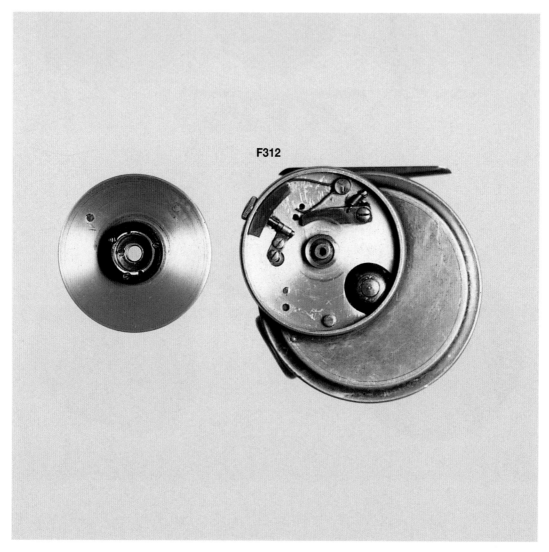

F312 ***** A 3⅜" Left Hand Wind St.George Multiplier with Silent Check, black handle, smooth brass foot, white agate lineguard, three screw drum latch and 2:1 multiplying action. Worn finish. Good. 1920's.

Uniqua

From 1903 the Uniqua was produced in sizes 2⅝", 2⅞", 3⅛", 3⅜", and 3⅝" and was similar in shape to a Contracted Perfect.

In 1909 the Uniqua Salmon appeared in sizes 3½", 3¾", 4" and 4½".

Both these models changed check mechanisms in 1917 to the Mk I Check and in 1923 to the Mk II Check.

In 1953 the 2⅝" and the 4½" were deleted.

In 1957 the 2⅞" was deleted and the whole line finished production in 1959.

G350 * A 4½" Uniqua with fat ivorine handle, brass foot, oval nickel silver drum latch stamped 'OIL' and 4 cusps on drum face. Retaining most finish. Excellent. Circa 1910.

G351 * A 3⅝" Uniqua with ivorine handle, polished alloy foot, horseshoe drum latch and single Check, although stamped 'Duplicated Mk II'. Finish worn. Good. Circa 1920.

G352 * A 3½" Uniqua with black handle, notched brass foot, wide drum, 'telephone' drum latch and Duplicated Mk II Check. Retaining most finish. Very good. Late 1930's.

G353 * A 3⅜" Uniqua with black handle, brass foot, horseshoe drum latch and Duplicated Mk II Check. Slight corrosion on backplate. Finish worn. Good. 1920's.

G354 ** A 2⅞" Uniqua with black handle, notched brass foot, telephone latch and Duplicated Mk II Check, but stamped Mk I. Finish lightly worn. Very good. 1920's.

G355 ** A 2⅝" Uniqua with black handle, brass foot, horseshoe drum latch and Duplicated Mk II Check (spare pawl missing). Finish lightly worn. Very good. 1920's.

Field

The Field was designed by Mr.W.Senior, the angling editor of the Field Magazine, and sold between 1895 and 1907 in eleven sizes from 2⅝" up to 5⅛".

Designed as a plain reel the benefit to the angler was that a fish could be braked by pressure of the fingers on the revolving rim of the face plate.

H375 *** A 4⅛" Field with fat ivorine handle, brass foot, bridges and drum. Retaining most finish. In leather case. Very good. Circa 1900.

H376 ***** A 3⅞" Prototype Field. With composition handle, brass foot and bridges. Brass face fixed by one central screw and stamped 'THE FIELD' 'Hardy's Pat' in unusual lettering. Alloy drum and backplate with raised face and enclosed oval logo. Note: The rim of this reel is fixed with the plate revolving inside it. It is unlike any Field I have ever seen. Retaining most finish. Superb. Mid-1890's.

Barton

Made between 1935 and 1940 the Barton, designed for Dr.Barton a president of the Fly Fishers Club in the 1930's, was a dry fly reel but would also have been useful for sea trout and light salmon work with its wide drum providing good line capacity. It had a specially designed offset foot which allowed the reel to sit without extending past the butt end of the rod, thus saving it from contacting the ground first when the rod butt was lowered.

I400 ***** A 3¼" Barton dry fly reel with black reverse tapered handle, offset notched brass foot, rectangular lineguard and three screw drum latch. Duplicated Mk II Check. Finish lightly worn. Very good. 1935-1940.

Tournament

Tournament casting became such an important medium for the Hardy brothers to prove their tackle in that they produced their own special Tournament reels.

In the Franco-British Exhibition of 1908 amongst all the other medals and honours won by Hardy tackle Mr.L.R.Hardy won eight bait casting championships.
It was titles such as these that proved the capability of Hardy tackle to all.

J425 ***** A 3¼" Trout Tournament Casting Reel with tiny alloy 'button' handles, alloy foot stamped L 4 with central hole and polished alloy bridges. The exceptionally light drum with widened core and central locking screw. The backplate with three separate controls for cast adjusting, L shaped pivoting lineguard and stamped 34364. Retaining most finish. In custom teak baize lined box. Excellent. 1920's.

I400

H375

H376

J425

St.John

Introduced in 1923 the St.John was a reel Mr.John James Hardy made for his own use for trout fishing with a lightweight rod. However the No.1 model with its greater line carrying capacity soon became used for lighter salmon work.

K450 ** A 3⅞" St.John No.2 with white composition handle, alloy foot, expanded drum core and three screw drum latch. Early Duplicated Mk II Check. Finish worn. Good. Circa 1925.

K451 * A 3⅞" St.John No.1 with black handle, notched brass oval foot, narrow drum core, three screw drum latch and Duplicated Mk II Check. Retaining most finish. In box. Very good. 1930's.

K452 ***** A 3⅞" St.John No.1 made of Hardy's Duralumin metal (aluminium beaten hard and highly polished to make it more resistant to saltwater and air corrosion). With black handle with counterbalance weight opposite, notched aluminium foot, narrow drum core and two screw drum latch. Duplicated Mk II Check. Excellent condition with some light scratching. Made for export this steelheader's reel belonged to Lee Straight a well known conservationist and steelhead angler in British Columbia: currently the President of their Steelhead Society (1987).
Purported to be one of only a dozen or less exported to Canada. 1930's.

Davy

The Davy is one of the rarest Hardy fly reels and was probably an adaptation of the Eureka trotting reel. The inventor, M.B.Davy Esq., wanted a fly reel with a narrower drum than Hardy made to give quicker line gathering and to balance the special dry fly rod Hardy made for him. The Davy was made from 1930 to 1939 in one size.

L475

L475 ***** A 3½" Davy fly reel with twin black handles, notched aluminium foot, telephone drum latch, multi-perforated drum face and Duplicated Mk II Check. The reel is scratched both inside and outside on the backplate. Very good. Early 1930's.

Sunbeam

The Sunbeam was made from 1924 until 1956 in 2¾", 3" and 3¼" sizes.

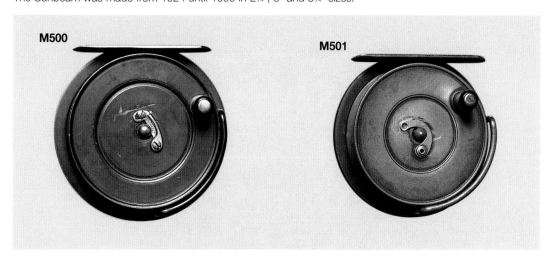

M500   M501

M500 * A 3¼" Sunbeam with black handle, brass foot, bronzed brass 'Bickerdyke' lineguard, telephone latch and single Check. Retaining most finish. Excellent. Late 1930's.

M501 * A 3" Sunbeam with black handle, brass foot and 'Bickerdyke' lineguard, horseshoe latch and single Check. Finish worn. Good. Circa 1930.

Hydra

The Hydra, an anagram of Hardy, was made from 1965 until 1967 in 3⅛" up to 4⅜" sizes.

N525 ** A 3½" Hydra narrow drum trout fly reel with black handle, alloy foot, two screw drum latch and single Check reversible to left hand use. Retaining most finish. Very good. 1965-1967.

N526 ** A 4⅜" Hydra salmon fly reel with black handle, notched brass foot, two screw drum latch and single Check reversible to left hand use. In box. Mint. Superb. 1965-1967.

Section O
Lightweight

The Lightweight was produced from 1936 to 1964.

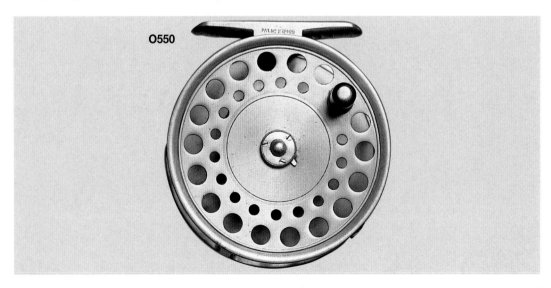

O550 ** A 3⅛" L.R.H.Lightweight trout fly reel with black handle, notched alloy foot, three screw drum latch and L shaped lineguard. Duplicated Mk II Check. Retaining very good silver anodised finish. Excellent. 1930's

Section P
Silex

The advent of The Silex, patented at the end of 1896, heralded the most major change to centrepin casting reels which, coupled with the Perfect, helped to lift Hardy's above the ranks of other tackle manufacturers.

The difference in casting performance with the Silex as against the normal wooden Starback reels was enormous and it was little surprise that anglers eagerly turned to this first model.

Many Silexes were made with a piece of the cage rim cut away to allow the angler to control casting with the use of the thumb against the revolving rim of the drum.

The Silex was made from 1896 to 1911 in 3", 3¼", 3½", 3¾", 4", 4¼" and 4½" sizes. The three control model (circa 1904 to 1910) combines blued springs and polished brass levers to make one of the most beautiful check mechanisms of any reel.

P575 ** A 4½" Silex with twin ivorine handles on crossbar with jewelled bearing, brass foot, caged drum and three rim controls and cut out rim section. Retaining most finish. Excellent. Circa 1905.

P576 *** A 4½" Silex with twin ivorine handles on crossbar with jewelled bearing, brass foot and caged drum. Extra wide model. Three rim controls and cut out rim section. Retaining most finish. Excellent. Circa 1905.

P577 ** A 4" Silex with twin ivorine handles mounted direct to drum face, jewelled bearing, brass foot, caged drum, three rim controls and cut out rim section. Retaining most finish. Excellent. Circa 1908.

P578 ** A 4" Silex with twin ivorine handles on crossbar with jewelled bearing, brass foot, caged drum, two rim controls and cut out rim section. Finish worn. Good. Circa 1902.

P579 *** A 3¼" Silex with twin ivorine handles mounted direct to drum face, jewelled bearing, brass foot, caged drum, three rim controls and cut out rim section. Finish worn. Very good. Circa 1908.

P575

Silex No.2

The Silex No.2 was a natural progression from The Silex, made from 1911 until 1921 in 2⅞" up to 4½" sizes.

Q600 * A 4" Silex No.2 with twin ivorine handles, brass foot, ivorine brake handle and three screw drum latch. Retaining most finish. Excellent. Circa World War I.

Q601 * A 4½" Silex No.2 with twin ivorine handles on fluted cups, brass foot, ivorine brake handle and slotted drum. Extra wide model for Mahseer fishing, etc. Retaining much finish with honest wear. In leather case. Excellent Circa 1912.

Q602 *** A 4½" Silex No.2 with twin ivorine handles on fluted cups, brass foot, ivorine brake handle, strapped tension screw and early left hand threaded knurled brass drum screw. Finish worn. In leather case. Very good. Circa 1912.

Q603 **** A 4½" Silex No.2 with twin white composite handles, brass foot (shortened at one end), ivorine brake handle, slotted drum and three screw drum latch. Solid drum face with one small hole. Finish lightly worn. Good. Circa 1913.

Q604 ***** A 3½" Silex No.2 with twin ivorine handles, brass foot, ivorine brake handle, strapped tension screw, early left hand threaded knurled brass drum screw and solid drum face with two small holes. Slight corrosion on drum core. Retaining most finish. In leather case. Very good. Circa 1911.

Q605 ** A 3¼" Silex No.2 with twin black handles, brass foot, horizontal ivorine brake handle for single-handed casting, strapped tension screw and three screw drum latch. Finish worn. Good. Circa 1912.

Q606 *** A 4" Silex No.2 with twin horn handles mounted on brass elliptical seatings. Made of walnut with brass foot running to brass starback on which is stamped 'The Silex No.2' and 'Hardy's Pat'. Brass 'Bickerdyke' lineguard, brake handle and telephone drum latch. Silent Check. The reel is complete and in mint condition. Superb. Circa 1912.

Section R
Silex Major

The Silex Major was made from 1923 until 1952 in 3" up to 4½" sizes.

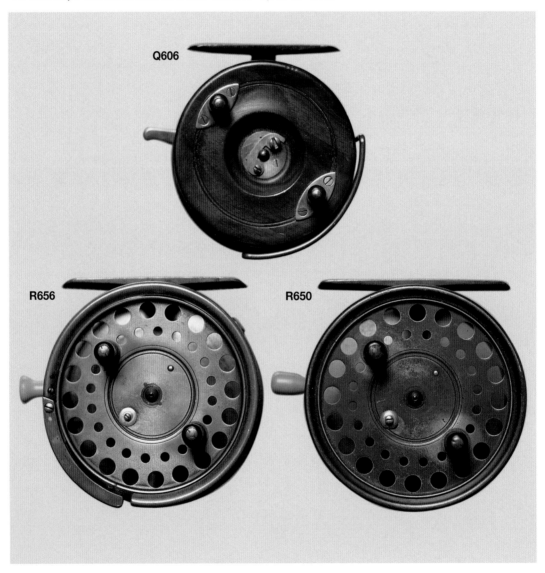

R650 ** A 4½" Silex Major with twin black handles, jewelled bearing, ivorine brake handle, brass foot and nickel silver weight casting regulator. Extra wide model. Retaining most finish. In leather case (strap broken). Excellent. Circa 1930.

R651 ** A 4½" Silex Major with twin black handles, jewelled bearing, ivorine brake handle, brass foot, nickel silver weight casting regulator and brass auxiliary rim brake. Worn finish. Good. Circa 1926.

R652 ** A 4" Silex Major with twin black handles, jewelled bearing, ivorine brake handle, brass foot and brass auxiliary rim brake. Worn finish. Good. Circa 1926.

R653 * A 4" Silex Major with twin black handles, jewelled bearing, ivorine brake handle, notched brass foot and ivorine quadrant weight casting regulator. Retaining most finish. Very good. Circa 1940.

R654 * A 3½" Silex Major with twin black handles, white composition brake handle, notched brass foot and ivorine quadrant weight casting regulator. Retaining most finish. Excellent. Post 1940.

R655 *** A 3" Silex Major with twin black handles, jewelled bearing, horizontal ivorine brake handle for single-handed casting, notched brass foot (slightly loose) and ivorine quadrant weight casting regulator. Face with the initials T.D.S-S neatly engraved. Finish worn. Fair. Circa 1930.

R656 **** A 4½" Silex Major with twin black handles, jewelled bearing, ivorine brake handle, notched brass foot, ivorine quadrant weight casting regulator and separate ivorine quadrant brake handle setting regulator with 7 positions. Brass auxiliary rim brake. The reel is stamped 'The Silex Major' and 'The Super Silex' both with patent numbers. Finish worn. Very good. Circa 1928.

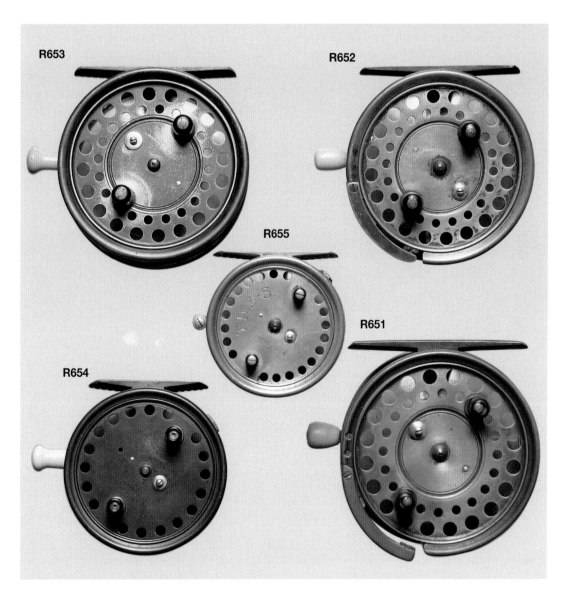

Section S
Silex Multiplier

The 1927 catalogue tells us that 'These reels are specially designed for casting light baits and are made in two sizes, 2¾" for trout, etc., and 3½" for salmon, etc. The winding action has a ratio of 2½ :1'.

It also informs us that the 2¾" version is used above the rod and the 3½" version used below the rod.

The Silex Multiplier, patented in February 1922, was sold from 1924 until World War II.

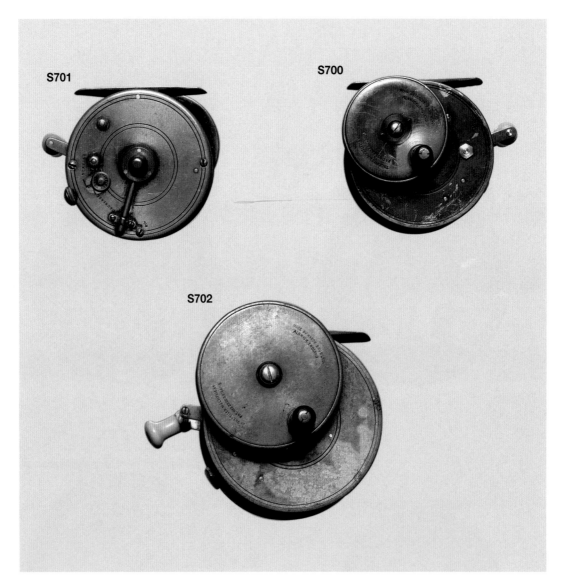

S701   S700

S702

S700 *** A 2¾" Silex Multiplier with black handle, waisted horizontal ivorine brake handle, notched brass foot and ivorine quadrant weight casting regulator. Retaining most finish with honest wear. Very good. 1930's.

S701 *** A 2¾" Silex Multiplier with black handle, waisted horizontal ivorine brake handle, brass foot and external brass oil pipe on backplate. Light finish with honest wear. Very good. 1920's.

S702 **** A 3½" Silex Multiplier with black handle, ivorine brake handle on large brass horizontal crossbar, brass foot, nickel silver brake indicator and external oil pipe on backplate. Finish with honest wear. Very good. 1920's.

Super Silex

The 1928 Catalogue, when talking of the development of the Super Silex after the Silex Major, tells us:

'Some three years ago, however, Hardy's developed a further improvement by which even the most inexperienced can make satisfactory casting, without any risk of over-running..... embodying all the features of the Silex Major and to add a simple action to enable the reel to be used when casting without touching any part of it'.

The Super Silex was made from 1928 until 1952 in sizes 3" up to 4½".

T750 *** A 3¾" Super Silex with twin black handles, ivorine brake handle, notched brass foot, ivorine quadrant weight casting regulator, two screw drum latch and solid unperforated face. Finish worn. Good. 1930's.

T751 *** A 3" Super Silex with twin black handles, jewelled bearing, ivorine brake handle, notched brass foot, ivorine quadrant weight casting regulator and extra catch on backplate to allow removal and replacement of drum. Worn finish. Good. 1930's.

T752 *** A 3½" Super Silex Multiplier with black handle, jewelled bearing, ivorine brake handle, notched brass foot, ivorine quadrant weight casting regulator and extra wide drum. Lightly worn finish. Very good. 1930's.

T753 ** A 3½" Super Silex Multiplier with reverse tapered black handle, jewelled bearing, ivorine brake handle, notched brass foot and ivorine quadrant weight casting regulator. Retaining most finish with honest wear. Very good. 1930's.

T754

T754 *** A 4½" Super Silex with extra-wide drum, twin black handles, jewelled bearing, ivorine brake handle, notched brass foot and ivorine quadrant brake casting regulator. Worn finish. 1930's.

Centerpin

The Combined Fly/Spinning reel was described in the 1897 catalogue as: 'The only perfect centre-pin spinning reel' and was a reel with: 'Compensating Steel Pivot Bearing, for Salmon, Mahseer, Trout, Pike, etc.'
It was certainly one of Hardy's earliest alloy reels and was made between 1894 and 1898.

U800 ***** A 4" Combined Fly/Spinning reel with twin ivorine handles on fluted cups, cageless revolving faceplate, brass foot and bridges, ON/OFF check on backplate with large projecting brass casting adjuster with central locking screw. Backplate stamped 'Hardy's Pat' and with enclosed oval logo. Finish worn. Good. Circa 1897.

U801 ***** A 4½" Combined Fly/Spinning reel with twin ivorine handles, cageless revolving faceplate, waisted brass foot with two perforations. ON/OFF check on backplate with large projecting brass casting adjuster with central locking screw. Backplate stamped with hand trademark, enclosed oval logo and 'Hardy's Pat'. Retaining most finish. In unnamed original leather case. Superb. Circa 1895.

U802 *** A 3½" Hardy Triumph casting reel with twin white composition handles, jewelled bearing, brass foot, slotted drum, nickel silver brake handle and casting weight adjuster. Stamped 'The Eureka Reel' this reel is one of the anomalies thrown up during reel development. One bad pit in rim. Finish worn. Fair. 1936 - 1951.

U803 ** A 4" Hardy Decantelle casting reel with twin black handles, black brake handle, notched brass foot and brass central drum locking screw. Retaining most finish with honest wear. Very good. 1930's.

U804 ** A 4" Silex Superba casting reel with twin black handles, black brake handle, notched polished alloy foot, ivorine quadrant weight casting regulator and two screw drum latch. In box. Retaining most finish. Excellent. 1950's.

Presentation

A Hardy presentation reel was often given to commemorate length of service, retirement, or to the winner of an angling contest. These reels were usually made with something different about them to set them apart from main production reels and turn them into an award to be treasured by the recipient.

V850 ***** A 3" Presentation reel in the 'Birmingham' style with ivorine handle. The reel is made from solid nickel silver with hand trademark and enclosed oval logo on the backplate and 'Ellem Fishing Club' and under 'WON BY' on the face plate, beautifully engraved with scroll decoration. There is no recipient's name. Ellem Fishing Club is one of the oldest in Britain. Excellent. Circa 1890.

W900 *** A 4½" Filey alloy surfcasting reel made on the Scarborough principle with twin black reverse tapered handles, brass foot with vertical arm to drum centre spindle. Arm stamped 'Hardy Bros Ltd., Makers, Alnwick, England'. No ratchet or lineguard. Drag controlled by large central knurled brass adjuster nut with central locking screw. Finish worn. Good. Circa World War I.

W901 **** A 5⅛" The Silex 'Ebona' ocean reel with twin bulbous ivorine handles mounted on nickel silver elliptical seats, ivorine brake handle, nickel silver plated foot running to elaborate starback and nickel plated brass 'Bickerdyke' lineguard. Nickel plated ON/OFF short rim control handle. The whole drum and backplate made of ebonite. The drum with central large knurled nickel plated drum adjuster with central locking screw. Beautifully elaborate internal nickel plated mechanism with felt lined brake. Mint. Superb. Circa 1912.

W902 **** A 5" Mahogany Longstone Starback reel with twin bulbous black handles mounted on triangular brass seatings, brass foot running to starback with 'Hardy Bros Ltd., Makers, Alnwick, England' stamped on it. Brass 'Bickerdyke' lineguard and brass rim brake lever handle with mahogany piece of almost 1" missing from rim at that point. Internal mechanism of basic Silex No.2 pattern. Honest wear. Good. Circa 1918.

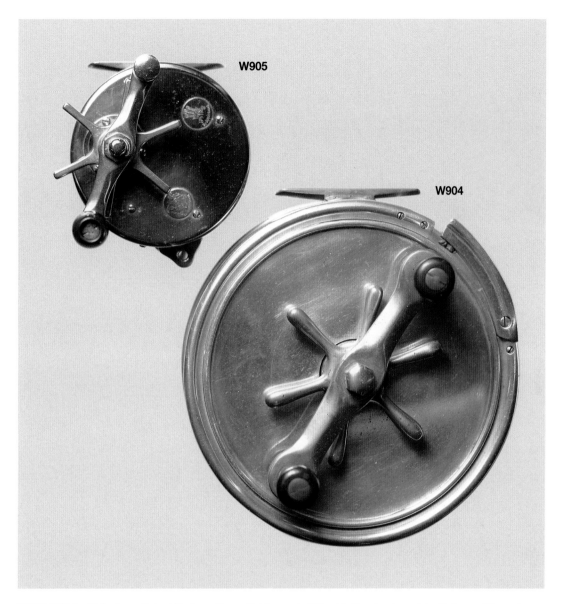

W905

W904

W904 ***** An 8" Andreas Patent Fortuna Game Fishing reel of Hardy's Duralumin metal with brass fittings. Large twin reverse tapered black handles on large brass crossbar over brass star drag adjuster held in place by two polished hardened steel locking nuts, the top one marked 'oil'. Brass foot fixed by eight nickel silver screws to Dural bridge. Brass supported Dural auxiliary rim control. Dual setting brass ratchet control lever along with Hardy, Fortuna and Andreas Pat.No 123405/18 stamps on backplate.

Two large and one small brass screws in drum core, one large one marked with an anti-clockwise arrow and 'GREASE'. Mint. Superb. Circa 1930.

W905 ***** A 4⅜" Zane Grey Game Fishing Reel. Although this is a later reel one cannot beat the description of the 1928 catalogue:

'Designed and manufactured to meet the requirements of the famous angler and author, Mr.Zane Grey….. In associating his name with this reel Mr.Zane Grey stipulated that it must be the best Big Game Fish Reel in the world.

It is constructed of genuine Monel Metal, the strongest non-ferrous metal known, and guaranteed to be absolutely immune to the action of sea water and air in any part of the world'.

The reel has black bulbous handle, star drag, brass spindle, hard leather line check/thumb protector, ON/OFF Check lever and circular Hardy Bros, Model, Size and 'To hold 600 yds. 9 thread' stamps on backplate. Mint. Superb. 1930's.

W903 *** A 4" No. 2 Goodwin beachcasting reel with twin black handles, black enamelled alloy foot, backplate and 'Bickerdyke' lineguard cast all in one. Silvery silk finished alloy drum. Nickel silver central drag adjuster with central locking screw not present on the No 1 model (1940-1953). Brass ON/OFF check adjuster on backplate. Circular stamps of Prince of Wales feathers, King George V's coat of arms and modern Hardy stamp on backplate. Mint condition in box. Superb. 1953 - 1959.

W906 ***** A 4¼" Andreas Patent Fortuna Game Fishing reel of Hardy's Duralumin metal with brass fittings. Twin reverse tapered handles on brass crossbar over circular knurled brass drag adjuster. Notched brass foot. Andreas Patent No.123405/18 stamped on backplate. Excellent. Circa 1931.

W907 ***** A 4¾" Silex No.2 "Pomeroy" West India Tarpon reel made entirely of brass with twin bulbous horn handles on nickel silver elliptical seatings, knurled central nickel silver drag adjuster, brass foot running to starback on backplate and brass rim mounted S shaped brake handle with ivorine knob. Heavy brass 'Bickerdyke' lineguard. Heavy duty internal brass mechanism with composite pad. 'The Silex No.2 Hardy's Pat.' and 'Hardy Bros. Ltd. Makers, Alnwick, England.' stamped on backplate. Named after Captain Edmund J.Pomeroy who wanted a reel strong enough for tarpon, sting ray and other hard fighting fish in the tropics. Mint. Superb. 1909-1913.

Altex & Hardex

The Altex, first catalogued in 1932, gave the angler the use of a fixed spool spinning reel with full bail arm from which the line could not escape, unlike the half bail arm reel.

The patent on this invention prevented all other makers from using the full bail arm.

The Hardex was a much cheaper reel with half bail arm which appeared five years later.

X950 * An Altex No.1 Mk V right hand wind with anti-reverse catch. Retaining most finish. Excellent. 1935-1950.

X951 ** An Altex No.2 (although not marked as such), early model with 'duck's foot' large removable plate on side of case. Tapered spool. Marked on backplate of flier Pat. No.373786 and Duplicated Mk II Check. Worn finish. Fair. Circa 1932.

X952 * An Altex No.2 Mk V left hand wind, mint in box with spare spool. Superb. 1935-1950.

X953 * An Altex No.3 Mk V left hand wind, mint in box with spare spool. Superb. 1935-1950.

X954 * A Hardex No.2 Mk 1, mint in box. Superb. Late 1930's.

X955 * An Altex No.3 Mk V left hand wind. Mint. 1950's.

X956 ***** An extremely early Altex with finger pick up and 'duck's foot' shape. Tapered black handle, left hand wind with ebonite drum. Marked on backplate of flier 'Made by Hardy Bros. Ltd. Alnwick, England' and 'Patent applied For'. Worn finish. Circa 1930.

Multiplying Baitcasters

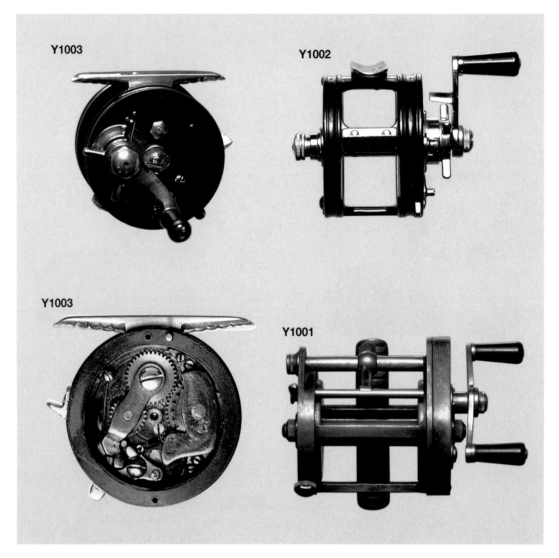

Y1000 * An Elarex level wind baitcasting reel with twin black reverse tapered handles on S shaped raised nickel silver crossbar, notched alloy integral foot with central hole, thumb support with Perspex water shield under. ON/OFF check, weight casting adjuster and oil port. Mint in box. Superb. Circa 1940.

Y1001 ***** A Silex Rex level wind baitcasting reel with notched brass foot and twin reverse tapered black handles on S shaped offset nickel silver crossbar, spindle oil holes in copper bush end mounts, nickel silver ratchet ON/OFF lever and rim mounted Check adjuster. Retaining most finish. In Hardy fibre box. Excellent. 1935-1937.

Y1002 **** A 2" Jock Scott non level wind baitcasting reel with reverse tapered black handle on curved offset chrome plated crank arm, chrome plated notched foot, chrome plated spindle end weight casting adjuster with jewelled bearing and marked 'oil', thumb support and ON or LOCKED rim and side mounted check adjusters. Black anodised finish. To be fished on single handed Jock Scott rod. Mint in teak box with own line winder with rod attachment. Superb. Late 1930's.

Y1003 *** A 2" Jock Scott non level wind baitcasting reel similar to Y1002 and stamped 'The "H.J.S." Brit.Pat No 486135'. Black anodised finish with dark blue rims. Own linewinder with rod attachment. Retaining most finish. In Hardy cardboard box. Excellent. 1940's.

Section Z
Cascapedia

One of the most sought after rare Hardy reels is the Cascapedia multiplying fly reel made from 1932 to 1939. Named after Canada's Grand Cascapedia river this unusual Hardy reel was made for export only and very few out of the 100 or so thought to have been made have surfaced.

Initially the reels were made from nickel silver with ebonite front and back plates and looked like the American Vom Hofe reels of the period. However the construction material was changed in 1936/7 to Hardy's Duralumin metal with a black anodised finish and the gear ratio was changed from 2½" to 1 down to 1¾" to 1.

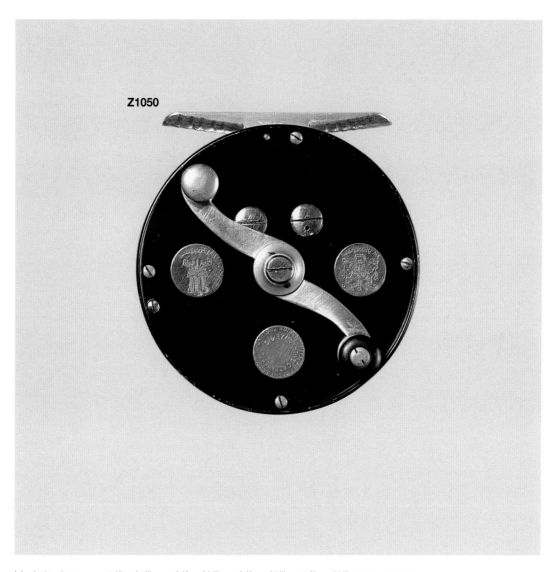

Z1050

Made in sizes: 1/0 - 3⅛"   2/0 - 3⅜"   3/0 - 3⅝"   4/0 - 3¾" (added in 1934)

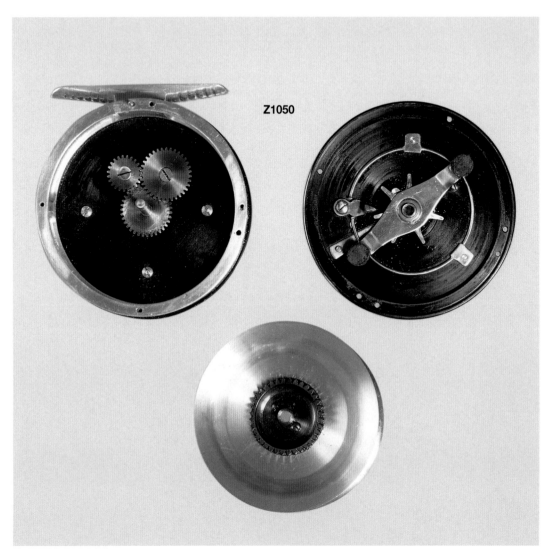

Z1050

Z1050 ***** A 4/0 (3¾") Cascapedia multiplying fly reel with black reverse tapered handle on Duralumin S shaped crossbar with nickel silver fixed central washer and counterbalance weight. Duralumin drum, notched foot and pillars (with one nickel silver roller pillar). Nickel silver knurled check adjuster on backplate with seven adjustable settings marked in red and ON/OFF ratchet control. The faceplate with three Duralumin circular stamps being:

'By appointment' with Royal Coat of Arms.

'Made by Hardy Bros. Ltd. Alnwick, England. The Cascapedia. Size 4/0'.

'By appointment' with Prince of Wales Feathers.

Retaining most finish with honest wear. Excellent. Circa 1937.

Z1050

Hardy Lures

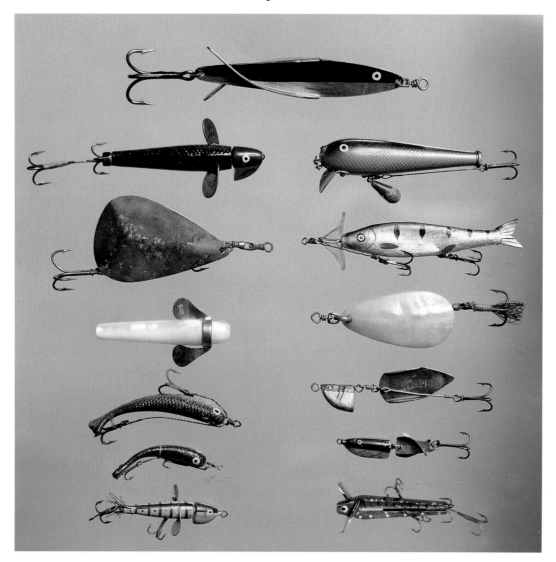

1909 Model Fly Minnow
Fly Minnow page 76

HARDY LURES

Beginning as far back as the early 1880's Hardy's began marketing a range of lures that, by the 1920's, had grown into a veritable horde. Throughout their history they were willing to manufacture new types of lures or paint their lures in specific colours to satisfy client's needs.

They stated in their 1894 catalogue:

'BAITS MADE TO ORDER: We will be pleased to make any special bait to order for any part of the world, but not less than 1 doz. of a size'.

After the turn of the century Hardy's became happy to make 'one-off' lures for clients who hunted exotic fish in far off lands and consequently there are individual lures in existence that are unique, especially some of those made for big game fishing. Hardy lures can be extremely rare and warrant close inspection by the collector.

One sign of a Hardy lure is the 'diamond' headed swivel, patented as an 'equilateral triangle' in 1901. There are Hardy lures not marked Hardy, such as Pearl Spoons, that can be identified by the diamond headed swivel. However collectors need to be sure that this diamond headed swivel has not at some time simply been attached to a non-Hardy lure as the company sold them separately for a considerable period. This guide will help avoidance of such anomalies.

The Hardy 'non-gyrating' diamond headed swivel first appeared in illustration on the Extra Heavy 'Kidney', 'Special' and 'Hog Backed' Spoons as late as the 1924 catalogue. There is no doubt though that the swivel was in use from the time of its Patent, telling us the catalogues cannot be taken as literal reference works.

The information in this section on Hardy lures is a study useful to the collector for identification and valuation purposes. Hardy lures are currently greatly undervalued and it is likely their value will rise substantially in years to come.

Some Noteworthy Hardy Patents

On the 24th November **1894** Mr.William Hardy and Mr.John James Hardy applied to Patent the design for a 'rotary device resembling a screw propeller, the latter, owing to the resistance of the water, rotating, whilst the fly does not rotate'. This was the propeller that would be fitted to Hardy's **Halcyon**, **Fly Minnow** and **Aaro** flies, etc. The complete specification was left November 24th 1894 and accepted December 29th 1894 number 4551.

On the 22nd February **1895** Mr.William Hardy and Mr.John James Hardy applied to Patent their design to make triangle (treble) hooks **with an eye at either end**, one in the middle where the stems of the three hooks diverged, so that gut or gimp could be passed through the eye 'at one extremity of the stem and then through the eye at the opposite extremity'.
The complete specification was left 22nd November 1895 and accepted 28th December 1895 number 3851.

On the 24th November **1899** Mr.William Hardy and Mr.John James Hardy applied to Patent their design for **rotatable fins** in order to be able to regulate a bait's spinning action for shallow, fast or deep and slow streams. The complete specification was left September 21st 1900 and accepted November 3rd 1900 number 23,482.

On the 9th May **1901** Mr.William Hardy and Mr.John James Hardy applied to Patent their design to **make baits better for casting** by changing the construction materials:

 'We construct the body of a metal having a considerably greater specific gravity than water. By suitably proportioning these materials, the **too rapid sinking of the bait may be prevented** (as with metal baits); while the operation of 'casting' is facilitated. In carrying out our improved method of manufacture, the body portion of the bait is built up, preferably from **lead and cork**, and comprises a core of lead about which a layer of cork is secured, the latter being painted or served with a covering of silk or soleskin which may be suitably painted.'

Next they applied to change the material used for constructing the fins:

'Hitherto the fins (or the parts which effect the spinning of the bait) have been composed of metal which, being hard, is liable to frighten the fish if touched by them. We therefore prefer to employ **India rubber or other**

suitable soft or compressible substance in their construction with a view to the fins yielding upon being gripped by the fish and thereby enabling the hooks or tackle to obtain a better hold. Fins of this character may be used in connection with tackles for mounting natural as well as artificial baits.'

Finally and most importantly they included the diamond headed swivel employed on many Hardy baits under this Patent

'**The eye of the swivel** to which the line or trace is attached is usually in the form of a ring which permits the attached line to move to one side out of the centre line of the bait and results in the bait being drawn through the water obliquely to the line or trace. This has a tendency to impart a 'wobbling' motion to the bait and is objectionable. To avoid this defect, we construct the eye in the form of an equilateral triangle, the apex being disposed at the fore end and serving **to receive and centralise the line or trace in relation to the axial line of the bait**.'

The complete specification was left on February 1st 1902 and accepted on March 6th 1902 number 9683.

On the 30th April **1909** Hardy Brothers and Charles Ashford of Birmingham applied to Patent a change to the construction of double, treble or multiple hooks whereby the shanks were brazed together but were then **twisted together to form a solid stem** before being hardened and tempered.

The complete specification was left October 26th 1909 and accepted February 3rd 1910 number 10,275.

On the 27th September **1909** John James Hardy, Laurence Robert Hardy and Hardy Brothers applied to Patent a two-piece construction for a spinning bait where the head and body were attached by a swivel joint and only the body was rotated by its fins, the head remaining still.

This was the beginning of the **'Keel Head'** lures.

The complete specification was left December 8th 1909 and accepted April 21st 1910 number 22,000.

On 17th July **1937** Hardy Brothers and Laurence Robert Hardy applied to Patent a **celluloid 'jacket'** for holding a natural bait and a celluloid vaned mount with central spear, either weighted or un-weighted. These jackets were made in clear, yellow or orange celluloid to allow for a change of colour for the bait as required.

The complete specification was left on December 18th 1937 and granted April 14th 1938 number 483,262.

On 8th October **1943** Hardy Brothers and Laurence Robert Hardy applied to Patent the construction of an artificial bait whereby the fin projecting down from the head to give the bait its action would be **constructed as one piece with the head** and not be a separate piece screwed to the head. Also the swivel would not be part of a separate piece screwed to the head, but attached to one wire to which is also attached the hook flight or **flights and plummet** and which is to be incorporated in the bait during moulding.

This Patent refers to Jock Scott Wiggler type baits. The body would be made in two pieces and joined either by a screw or push fitting.

'The bait can be moulded in any suitable plastic, but preferably a transparent mouldable material is used, for example the material sold under the Registered Trade Mark "Perspex".… if desired the bait can be solid and not hollow.'

The complete specification was left on October 13th 1944 and granted January 11th 1945 number 566,753.

The Phantom's Progress:

The Phantom Minnow	1883 - 1885	9 sizes up to 4¾"
The Famed Phantom	1885 - 1888	9 sizes up to 4¾"
The Silk Phantom	1888 - 1896	1¾", 2", 2¼", 2¾", 3¼", 3¾", 4¼", 4¾"
The SoleSkin Phantom	1888 - 1901	1¾", 2¼", 2½", 3", 3½", 4", 4½"
The M.C.Phantom	1894 - 1901	1¾", 2", 2¼", 2¾", 3¼", 3¾", 4¼", 4¾"
The Horn Phantom	1899 - 1909	1½", 1¾", 2¼", 2½", 3", 3¼", 3¾", 4", 4½", 5"
The Rubber Phantom	1900 - 1909	1½", 1¾", 2", 2¼", 2¾", 3¼", 3¾", 4¼", 4¾"
The Special Phantom	1902 - circa 1940	1¾", 2", 2¼", 2½", 2¾", 3", 3¼", 3½", 4", 4½", 5"
The Patent Ideal Phantom	1902 - circa 1940	1½", 2", 2¼", 2½", 2¾", 3", 3¼", 3½", 4", 4½"
The Chilwa Phantom	1907 - 1911	4", 5", 6"
The Hardy Phantom	1910 - circa 1940	2½", 3", 3½", 4"
The Hutton-Wye Phantom	1921 - circa 1940	3", 3¼", 3½", 3¾"

**** **The Phantom Minnow**, **Famed Phantom** and **Silk Phantom** were the same lure.

**** **The SoleSkin Phantom** was the same lure again, but made with soleskin instead of silk.

**** **The M.C. Patent Phantom** was mounted with an internal Patent Combination Swivel, on the ball bearing principle, was made of 'transparent' soleskin and had a silvered lead inside.

The M.C. appears to have been the first Phantom to have been offered by Hardy's with a swivel at its head.

**** **The Horn Phantom**, with its body made from horn, was more durable than the normal silk or soleskin Phantoms, the 4½" and 5" being made to order only.

**** **The Rubber Phantom** was available in 9 sizes from 1½" to 4¾"and looked the same as the Silk and Soleskin Phantoms, except that its body was of rubber construction. It had a hole in its underside to allow shot to be added for weighting

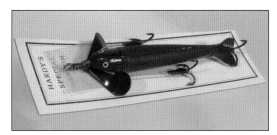

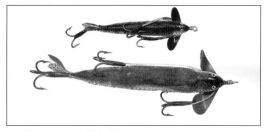

*** **The Special Phantom** was the original Phantom, Famed Phantom and Silk Phantom but with the addition of a Geen's swivel at the head.

Lure photography: Dave Watson

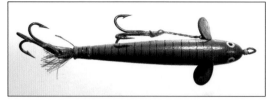

*** **The Ideal Phantom** had a cork surrounded lead core covered with a silk 'skin' or painted. This method of construction gave the Phantom better weight for casting along with buoyancy so that the lure did not sink too quickly. It had 'hook mounts soldered to the head' so that 'side mounts of ordinary strength (6d.each) can be slipped on to replace any frayed out by simply passing the gut loop through the side eyes of the bait'.

***** **The Chilwa** was a version of the Ideal Phantom with a fin on its back towards the tail, early drawings of which indicate it might have been made to imitate a baby Tarpon. The Chilwa was the only Phantom to have fins on its body and is a rare lure to find with the fins intact.

**** **The Hardy Phantom**, with its metal Keel Head and body construction the same as the 'Ideal' Phantom's, with a lead centre, cork surround and outer silk skin, first appeared as the **'1910' Model Hardy Phantom**. It became the **Hardy Anti-Kink Phantom** in 1917, with a 4" size appearing by 1923.

Pictured above is a later **Hardy Anti-Kink Phantom** with silk body (pre-1924) that has interestingly been called the 'Keel Head Phantom' by Hardy's as can be seen on the card, although it does not appear to have been catalogued as such.

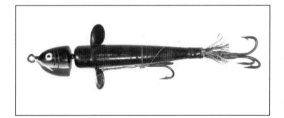

**** In **1924 a smooth metal body** took over from the silk skinned 1910 Model construction, but for that one year of 1924 the lure was still called Hardy's 'Anti-Kink' Phantom (see Keel Head Devons section).
In 1925 this smooth metal bodied Keel Head was called **'The Hardy Phantom'** once again and was offered until the 1940's.

Hardy Phantom showing different head shape.

Keel Head Devons

*** **The 1914 Model 'Anti-Kink' Devon** was a metal-bodied evolution of the 1910 Model Hardy Phantom which allowed the body to revolve whilst the head, with its weighted lower 'keel', remained still, hence later becoming known as a 'Keel-Head' Devon. The metal body was 'scaled by deep impressions with a punch, which gives it a realistic effect, and as the colouring matter is seated deeply into the scaled part it cannot be rubbed off.' Anti-Kink Devons were called Hardy Devons after 1924 and were offered into the 1940's.

**** Over time various head shapes were made including this rarer style of 'Flat Head' Hardy Phantom pictured on the right. Note the long vertical triangular shape of the head, weighting it at the bottom.

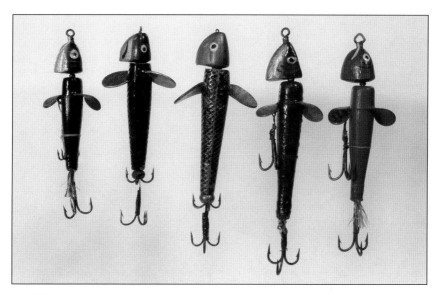

The second and third lures from the left are 'scaled body' 1914 Model Anti-Kink Devons which became 'Hardy Devons' after 1924. The lure on the left and the two on the right, with their smooth bodies, are Hardy Phantoms (1924 to 1940's).

*** **The Hutton-Wye Phantom (1921 Model)** had a free moving hook mount, allowing the Phantom to slip up the line once a fish was hooked.

'The metal head, with fans (fins), is made in one piece and under our Patent No.155523. The tail is formed of strands of gut, and is most realistic'. It was designed with the co-operation of Mr.J.A.Hutton, author of 'Rod Fishing for Salmon on the Wye'.

The Hutton-Wye Phantom ended its run at the end of the 1930's.

Devons

A Mystery Solved
by Jess Miller, John Ayers and John Drewett

***** **Hardy's Transparent Amber Devons** were catalogued from 1895 to 1911 in sizes 1", 1¼", 1½", 1¾", 2", 2½" and 3", but they are so rare collectors have had difficulty in establishing their true identity. They were not made of real Amber as it was too soft, but of a hard and fairly brittle, glass-like material that could easily have been broken during use.

 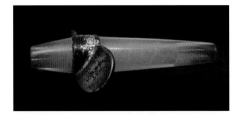

Here is the rare **Transparent Amber Devon** in all its glory with banded silver plated fins. In natural light the glass is almost clear (photos Leif Erixon).

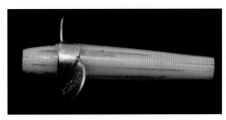

***** Here is the rare '**Maori Inanga**' variation of the Transparent Amber Devon with banded silver plated fins. It was made in sizes 1½", 1¾" and 2" of striated Xylonite for export to New Zealand to imitate the 'Maori Inanga' (galaxius maculatus), a small whitish fish with a brown streak down its side, one of five species that form the bulk of the NZ whitebait catch in rivers and streams.

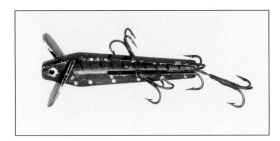 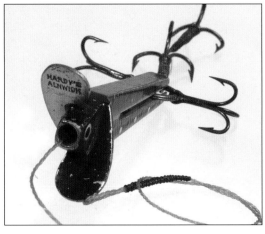

***** **The 'Forward' Rectangular Devon**, catalogued from 1906 to 1909, was available in all silver or 'coloured' and in 1", 1¼", 1½", 1¾", 2¼", 2½" and 3" sizes and is a rare Hardy lure.

The Pennell Minnow, invented by Mr.Cholmondeley-Pennell, was catalogued by 1894 and described as a Devon in which 'the hooks spin with the bait'.

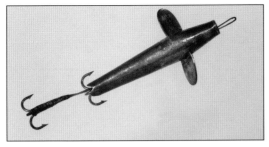 

*** An early Pennell Devon with fluted end.

*** This **1909 Model Aluminium Pennell** appeared in 1910.

** An **Improved Pennell Devon 1914 Model** with the body scaled with a punch.

*** **Pioneer Devons** had appeared in the catalogues by 1902.

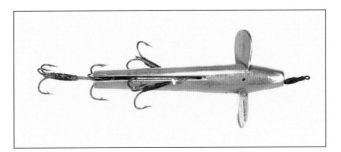

Pioneer Devon showing early hook mount.

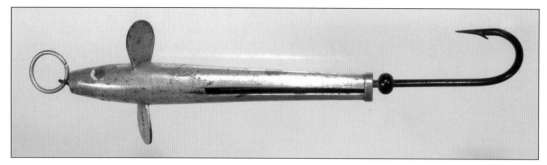

**** A 4½", silver finished, Pioneer Devon rigged with the strong single hook option for Mahseer fishing. 1930's.

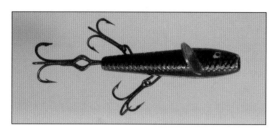

** **The Improved 'Pioneer' Devon** was being offered by 1914 with its body 'scaled by deep impressions made with a punch, giving a realistic effect and allowing the paint to seat more deeply' just as with the 1914 Model Anti-Kink Devon and the Improved 1914 Model Pennell Devon.

*** **The Improved Pioneer** used a spring steel 'unbreakable' mount to carry the hooks and retain them in position. Note the tail end treble with its 'basket' feature to 'lock' into the end of a Devon, especially those with fluted ends.

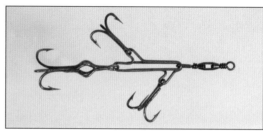

** **Threadline Pennell Devons** were offered in the late 1930's in five sizes from ⅝" to 1⅛" in Silver, Silver and Red, Blue and Silver, Brown and Silver and Brown and Gold colours.

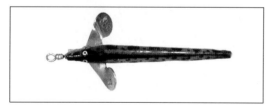

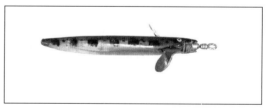

** **Hardy Quill Devons** were available for an extraordinarily long period, catalogued from as early as 1888 to well into the 1960's, a testament to their effectiveness.

**** **The Beadnell Spinner** was a copper sea lure with a lead head 'the tail can be set to give a quick or slow spin as desired'. 1923 – 1934 in 3", 3½" and 4½" sizes as here.

** **The Golden Sprat Devon** ('Spratt' Devon in the catalogue illustrations) appeared in 1925 and became a popular lure. In either gold or silver it was made with metal or Perspex fins and available in 2", 2½", 3", 3½" and 4" sizes.

** A later **Golden Sprat Devon** that replaced the original around 1951 and ended in 1961.

**** Catalogued as the **Herring or Sprat Bait** from 1925 to 1934 in 6", 8" or 10" sizes (this is a 10" with one of its smaller compatriots. Note that this lure could be specially made in larger sizes or painted in any colour to order.

 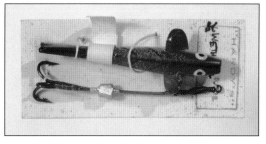

*** **The 'Wetheral' Bait** that arrived in 1927 until the 1940's was made entirely of a flexible material like India rubber with flexible fins integral with the body. It was available in Brown and Gold, Blue and Silver, Golden or Silver Sprat colours and in sizes 2½", 3" and 3½".

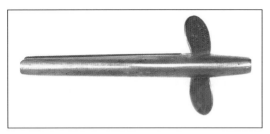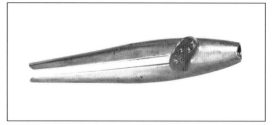

**** **The 'Murdoch' Oval Devon** designed by a late Editor of the 'Scottish Field' was offered in blue and silver, brown and gold or plated silver or plated gold and first appeared in the French 1908 catalogue, but only featured in catalogues until 1912.

* **'Heavyweight' Devons** for Threadline Fishing were catalogued from the late 1930's to the early 1960's. Made of heavy alloy they aided long distance casting.

* **The 'Reflex' Devon**, 1924 to the mid-1950's, was made in 'Light' or 'Heavy' weights in aluminium colour or gold and silver sided, as here.

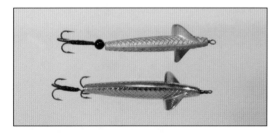

* **The 'Sprat-Devon'** was designed in 1936, appeared in the 1937 catalogue and was sold into the mid-sixties. It became an extremely popular lure available in right or left spin, seven sizes from 1½" to 3½" and silver, half silver, half silver half gold, blue and silver and brown and gold colours.

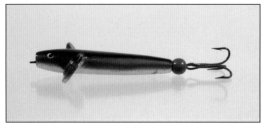

* **The 'West Country'** Devon catalogued from 1952 had an oval back and belly, was after an original by Captain C.L.Clayton and was offered in Brown and Gold and Blue and Silver in 1½", 2" and 2⅜" sizes.

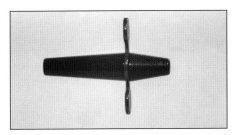 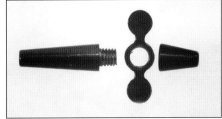

*** **Rose's Reversible Spin Devon**, 1954 to 1959, allowed a simple method of changing the spin by reversing the fins. Supplied with flat fins, as here, the angler twisted these to his favour by use of a special key. In sizes 1¼", 1½" and 2".

* **The 'Hardy Strathallan' Devon** appeared in 1963 moulded in one piece from special plastic material. The mount had a metal sleeve fitted at the top of the treble hook to prevent bending and a retaining ring held the swivel eye. Sizes: 2", 2¼", 2½", 2¾" and a variety of colours: Gold, Black and Gold, Red and Gold, Brown and Gold, Silver, Red and Silver, Ox Blood and Silver, Rainbow Trout and Natural Minnow.

 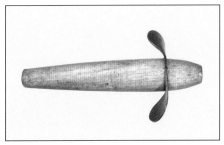

*** I call these uncatalogued copper finned devons the **'Wood Devon'** but their period of manufacture is difficult to pinpoint although it was likely to have been during the 1940's when austerity measures were in place nationally and paint was hard to get.

 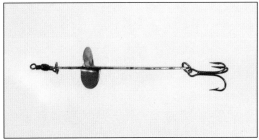

** An interesting flat bodied post-war metal Devon with the Hardy logo enclosed in a rectangular box.

Fly Minnow

** **The 1909 Model Fly Minnow** was available in Silver, Blue and Silver and Brown and Silver in nine sizes from 1" to 4½". In 1927 it became simply the Model Fly Minnow and was marketed into the late 1950's.

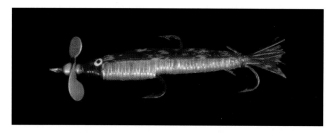

** Not to be confused with this **Fly Minnow** for use with a fly rod that was catalogued from the early 1890's to the early 1960's, at which time a version with a red, silver ribbed body 'the Ythan' was also available.

Swallow Tails

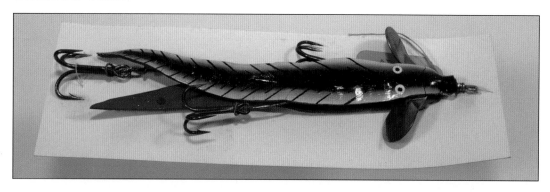

** **The New 'Swallow Tail' Rubber Bait** first appeared in 1903 and was available in a range of standard colours as well as colours to order in ten sizes from 2" up to 7" in ½" steps except between the 6" and 7" sizes.
The 2" to 4½" sizes were mounted with gut and the 5" to 7" sizes mounted with gimp during the lure's earlier years.
During the mid to late 1930's a Threadline Swallow Tail was marketed in sizes 1¼" and 1½".
Swallow Tails were marketed into the early 1950's.

Lead Heads

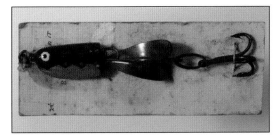 

*** **The 'Swimmer' Bait 1924 Model** was still being marketed in the mid-1950's.

*** **The 'Hardy' Spoon** appeared in the 1925 catalogue, but was changed to the version where the spoon part gained crimped up sides circa 1932 and was offered to the end of the 1950's.

Spoons

 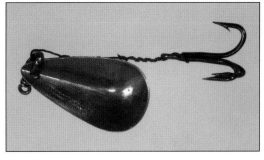

***** This rare spoon was not catalogued however research has found it to be a Hog Backed Bar Spoon from circa1894. The larger one is not stamped Hardy's, but indicates the 'bar' mounting this research was pointing to. Perhaps we should rename it the **Hog Backed Pattern Spoon** to avoid confusion with later Hog Backed Spoons.

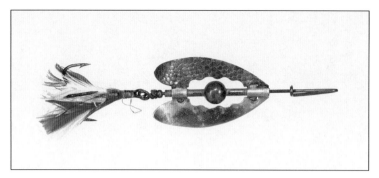

**** An **Alnwick Spinner** is mentioned in the 1883 catalogue, however there is no mention of it again until 1895, when it was offered in blue and silver, but it is highly unlikely that this was the same spinner. The Alnwick Spinner would seem to have been bought in by Hardy's, as with the example shown, who then re-dressed the hooks to their own pattern. We may never know what the lure was that was mentioned in the 1883 catalogue as it was not illustrated. The Alnwick Spinner disappeared from the catalogues towards the end of the 1890's.

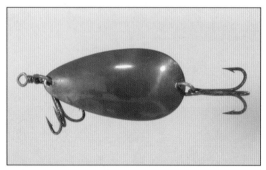 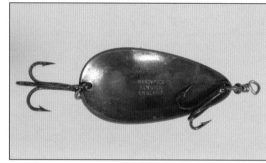

** An 'Ordinary' Spoon Bait, available in eight sizes, was catalogued as early as 1888 and was the forerunner of this **Special Extra Heavy Spoon** with its silver inside and copper outside that was catalogued by 1900 in 1½", 1¾", 2", 2¼", 2½", 2¾" and 3" sizes.
Offered for a long time by 1951 it had been renamed the 'Hardy Special Spoon'.
By 1954 sizes were down to 1½", 1¾", 2", 2¼" and 2½" which by 1963 had changed again and were limited to 2", 2½" and 3" before it disappeared from the catalogues.

**** A **Kidney or Special Spoon** mounted with a single forged steel eye hook and a clip on the inside of the lure to hold the hook in place is one of Hardy's Special Bait options for Tiger Fish dating from circa 1917 to 1924.

***** In 1894 a Hog-Back Flying Bar Spoon and a Hog-Back Revolving Spoon were being sold.

Hog-back Flying Bar Spoon   Hog-back Revolving Spoon

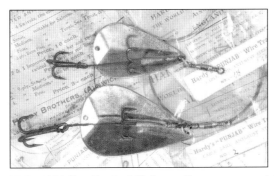
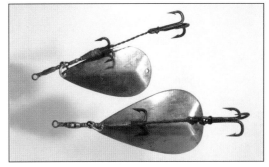

*** By 1900 **Hog Backed Mahseer Spoons** were catalogued in 1", 1½", 2", 2½" and 3" sizes and 'gold outside, silver inside'.

There were also Small Flying Spoons that had the same shape as the Hog Backs in ½", ¾" and 1" sizes, but these were offered as all silver in colour, although gold ones exist, and had a single hook mounting as opposed to the Hog Back's one or two treble hooks wire mounted in tandem, depending on the size of the lure.

*** In 1924 Spoons were illustrated for the first time fitted with the Hardy Non-Gyrating Swivel (now called the Hardy Swivel) patented back in 1901, but it is some ten years later before the catalogues mention this development: '**Mahseer Mounts** of 2", 2½" and 3" – 'Hogbacked' Spoons are now fitted with an additional 'Hardy Swivel', which eliminates all danger of the wire mount becoming untwisted'.

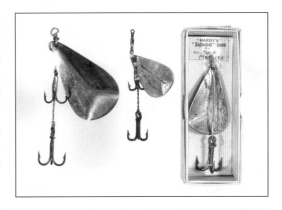

The Hog Backed Spoons remained catalogued in the same way until 1954 when they were reduced to only 1" and 2" sizes before being dropped from the catalogues by 1960.

**A later Hog Backed Spoon showing the Hardy logo in enclosed rectangle.

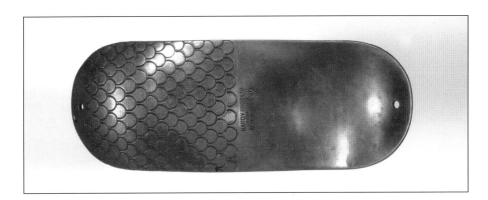

***** **The Professional Spoon** 'made after the pattern used by the professional fishermen at Vancouver. It is half convex and half concave. The mounting is one large single hook fastened to the end of the spoon.' Made in 5" only this one measures 1¾" wide. Circa 1920. Extremely rare.

The Norwegian, Silver Devon, Extra Heavy Special, Extra Heavy Kidney and Hog Backed Spoons, etc., of the late 1920's and 1930's were made of Sheffield Plate (silver rolled onto copper) with gold being deposited onto the silver or copper when required, some were also made of Duralumin.

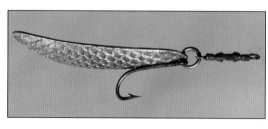

*** **The Special 'Norwegian' Scaled Spoon**, scaled over its complete outer body, made to Captain Radclyffe's pattern in broad or narrow patterns in 2¼", 2½" and 3" sizes was first catalogued in 1910 and lasted to around the end of the 1930's. This one lacks its main hook and mount.

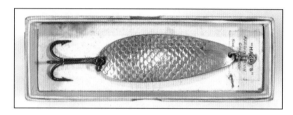

*** **The 'Bergen' Spoon**, scaled outside over some four fifths of its body, appeared in the early 1920's until the end of the 1930's.

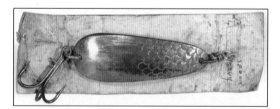

** **Special Extra Heavy Kidney Spoons**, scaled over approximately half of their outer body appeared by 1900. Initially offered in sizes 1½", 2¼", 2½", 2¾" and 3" a 1¾" had crept in by 1905 and a 1" and 1¼" by 1911, making eight sizes in all.
Catalogued as 'copper outside, silver inside' throughout the lure's history a 'gold outside, silver inside' version was the only one on offer by 1952 in sizes 1", 1¼", 1½", 1¾", 2¼", and 2½", but by 1960 this had changed back to 'copper outside, silver inside' before the lure's long run ended in 1963.

*** **The 'Wilson' Spoon** for Big Game Fish made its appearance in 1925 in 4", 4½", 5" and 6" sizes and was last catalogued in the 1953 Big Game Supplement.

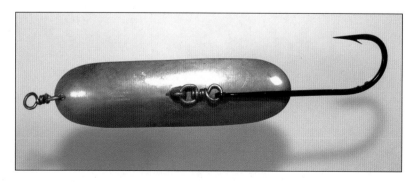

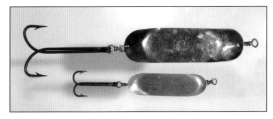 

*** **The 'Stewart' Spoon** for Big Game Fish appeared in 1925 in 3", 3½", 4", 4½" and 5" with a 6" appearing in 1928 and was last catalogued in the 1953 Big Game Supplement.

*** **'Silver Devon' Bar Spoons** appeared in 1924 in 1½", 2", 2½" and 3" sizes and had been 'developed with the co-operation of 'Silver Devon', author of 'Pike Fishing, Red Letter Days and others.' The bar was mounted with red beads and the hook could be changed at will due to the use of a Hardy's 'Attachment' Link. Colours were 'red inside with yellow, green and blue broad diagonal stripes on back, or copper one side, silver the other' and 'the tassle at hook is made of gut dyed red'

** In 1928 the red beads were replaced by a series of links that 'eliminated breakage' and which were 'kept in a rigid position by means of a soft copper wire interlaced through the links'. Along with this change for the first time the lure was illustrated with a straight 'flattened' leading edge.

** In 1951 came the final change, despite the catalogue description contradicting the new illustration for that year by still referring to 'links', in that the links bar was replaced by a straight wire mount made of Hardy's 'special Punjab Wire fitted with one Round Bend Treble Hook and finished off with a red gut tassel'.

The Silver Devon Bar Spoon disappeared from the catalogues in 1960.

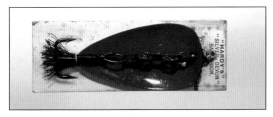

'Silver Devon' Bar Spoon with Hardy's 'Attachment' Link between the red painted chain and treble hook. 1928 - 1951.

Post 1928 Bar Spoon.

Bar Spoons showing different mounts, the top one pre-1928 and the bottom one post 1928.

* The 1960's 'Tube' Spoon, made in collaboration with J.F.Ham of Birmingham allowed the tube and spoon to ascend the line, like a Devon, after a fish was hooked.

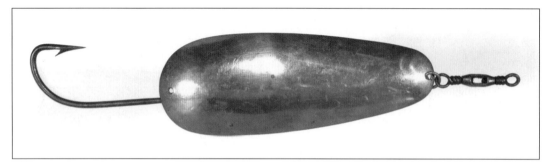

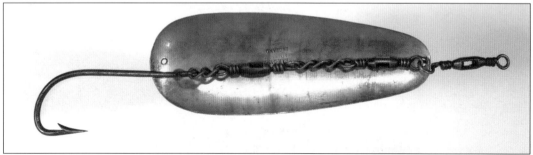

**** **The 'Indian' Spoon** for Tyhee fishing (catalogue spelling) in British Columbia and angling for Tiger fish first appeared in 1909 and was catalogued until 1934. Of the 2½", 4" and 5" sizes this is the 5" example showing the earlier double swivel hook mounting.

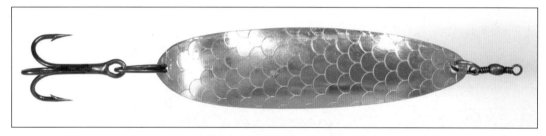

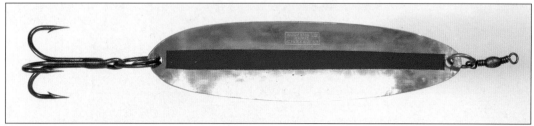

*** **The 'Jim Vincent Broads' Spoon** was a highly successful 1½ oz. 5¾" long pike spoon (although it certainly accounted for many other species). Sold between 1950 and 1960.

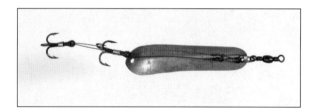

* The Hardy **Greenwell Spoon** appeared in 1951 and was marketed into the mid-1960's. Made plain in the catalogues was the instruction 'Do not polish this spoon'. The Greenwell was a 2½" lure with silver and copper sides.

Pearl

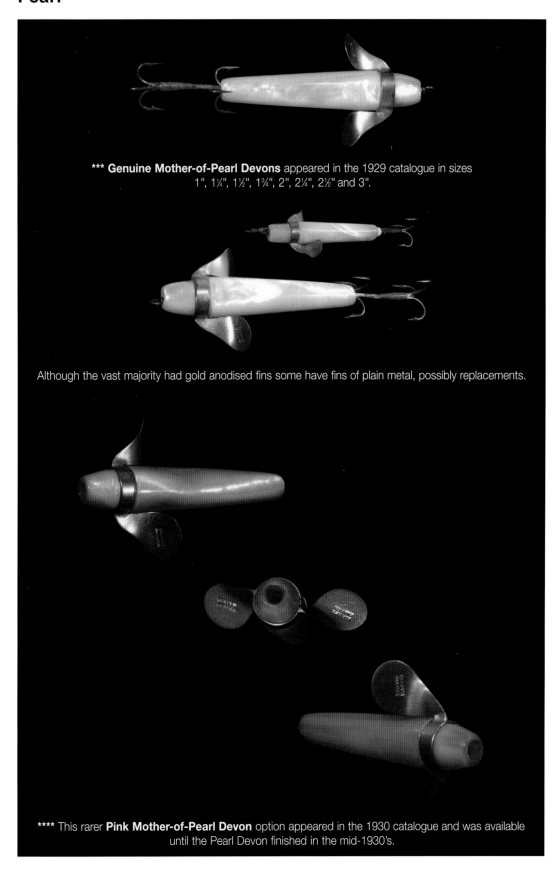

*** **Genuine Mother-of-Pearl Devons** appeared in the 1929 catalogue in sizes
1", 1¼", 1½", 1¾", 2", 2¼", 2½" and 3".

Although the vast majority had gold anodised fins some have fins of plain metal, possibly replacements.

**** This rarer **Pink Mother-of-Pearl Devon** option appeared in the 1930 catalogue and was available
until the Pearl Devon finished in the mid-1930's.

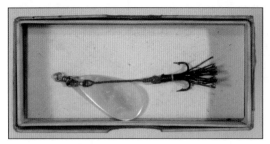

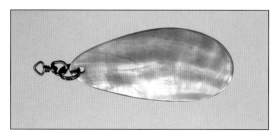

*** **Pearl Spoons** were catalogued from 1928 to the end of the 1930's and were offered in sizes 1", 1¼", 1½", 2", 2½" and 3".

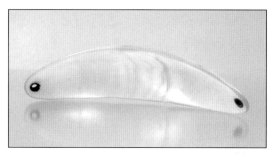

***** A unique experimental 4" Hardy Pearl Spoon that was never catalogued or offered for sale by the company.

Plugs

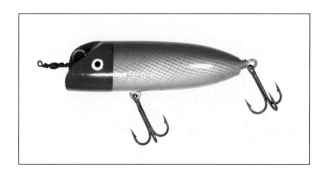

*** **Darting and Diving Baits** were marketed from 1929 to around the end of the 1930's. Initially in 3½", 4" and 5" sizes by 1934 their range was expanded to 2", 2½", 3", 3¼", 4", 5", 6", 7" with the 3½" having disappeared.

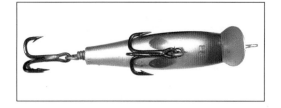
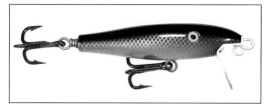

*** Hardy **'Wigglers'** were floating baits that appeared for a short period in the late 1930's and were available as a one-piece or two-piece bait, the one-piece in sizes 2½", 3" and 4" and the two-piece in sizes 3" and 4".

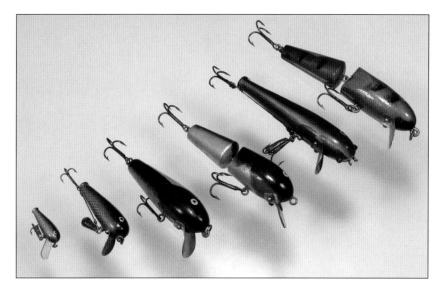

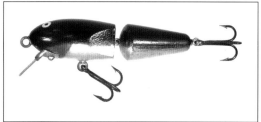

** **Hardy-Jock Scott 'Wigglers'** (1951) were floating lures that were 'keeled' either with lead wire around the double or treble hook beneath the body or by the addition of special weights (plummets). In 1951 sizes were 1", 1¼", 1½", 1¾", 2", 2½", 3" and 3½" and colours offered were: Blue back and silver belly; brown back and gold belly; slate-grey back, silver belly with green tinge on side; blue back with ivory belly. They were catalogued up to 1958.

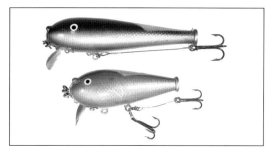

Wake Lures

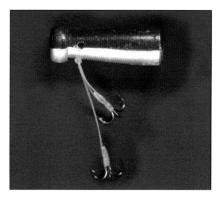

**** **The 'Wake' Lure** was quite a rare sea trout lure fished from a fly rod. Early 1950's.

**** **The No.2 Wake Lure** for sea trout fishing with a fixed spool reel is also quite rare. Early 1950's.

Flexibles

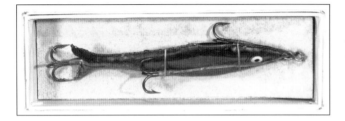

*** A hand sewn **Flexible Sprat Bait** circa 1930.

** This **Flexible Sprat** was made of 'flexible material' and was designed to be mounted on any one of a number of Hardy tackles without spinning fins, unlike this one, proving this lure's versatility. The tail on this one has been clipped. Catalogued from 1929 to 1937 the Flexible Sprat was available in Silver, Gold and also Gold with Silver belly and cross stripes in red and 3", 3½" and 4" sizes.

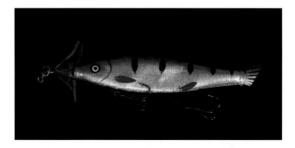

Halcyons

*** The **Original Halcyon** was marketed from as early as 1883 up to 1929 and had a propeller that was fixed as part of the lure's body. Described as 'having been designed from the large Alexandra fly' in 1903 the Halcyon was offered in Gold as well as Silver (propeller colour) as 'reports from India show these to be excellent Mahseer baits'.
** The **Improved Halcyon**, identified by its independently spinning propeller, had appeared by 1900 and was marketed all the way to the mid-1950's. They were offered in sizes up to 3", but special order sizes could be made up to 6".

***** An extremely rare 5" Improved Halcyon, most likely made for Mahseer fishing, along with one of a much more common size.

Sylphs

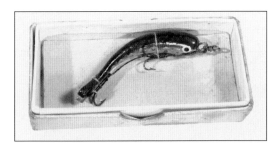 

**** The **New 'Sylph' Minnow**, made of flexible material, appeared in 1925 in 1½" to 3½" sizes. 'The head hook is fixed to the minnow with an Emery fastener, as per the Sand Eel spinners, and the swivel is of the Hardy non-gyrating design'. Sylphs were still being offered at the end of the 1930's.

Soleskin

**** The **Soleskin Sprat or Brit** was catalogued from 1900 to 1921.

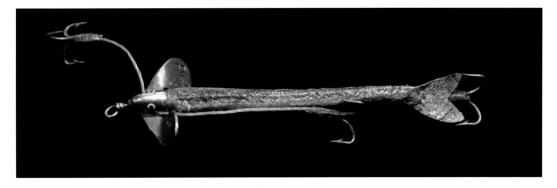

*** The **Silver Sand Eel** started in 1902 and changed from soft rubber to Soleskin in the 1907 season and was offered into the end of the 1930's in sizes 2¾", 3½", 3¾" and 4½".

Set up by John Drewett for son Chris

Can you identify the Hardy Lures and Mounts in this display?

Hardy Spoon	Halcyon	Sylph
SwallowTail	Aaro	Jock Scott Wiggler
Pearl Spoon	Single Soleskin Bait	Special Phantom
Silver Devon Bar Spoon	Ideal Phantom	Sand Eel Wobbler
Golden Sprat Devon	Natural Bait Spinner	Wee Murdoch Spinner
Fly Minnow	Corkscrew Spinner	Natural Bait Spinner
Natural Bait Spinner	Hardy Swimmer	Golden Sprat Devon
Sand Eel Tail Spinner	No.2 Wake Lure	Prawn Spinning Mount
Fly Minnow 1909 Model	Special Phantom	Silver Sand Eel
Ideal Phantom	Crocodile	
Leather Eel Tail Spinner	Keel Head Anti-Kink Devon	

To register your interest in future updates to these Price Guides or to be notified about future publications please go to: **http://www.HardyReelBook.com** or send your contact details to: Jess Miller, c/o Classic Angling Magazine, PMA House, Free Church Passage, St.Ives, Huntingdon, Cambridgeshire, PE27 5AY, UK.

The Dunkeld Collection Price Guide 2004

Qualification

Great care has been taken over the accuracy of this price guide however prices are given as a guide only due to reels sometimes selling for higher or lower prices than those stated.

Bracketed prices give the range within which a particular reel model has sold most recently.

Bracketing also encompasses prices realised for reels that vary in condition from those in the collection.

Prices have been gathered from auction sale results and prices of sales concluded at vintage tackle shows, etc., and are given in Pounds Sterling. Please use the prevailing exchange rate to calculate the value in your country.

Section A
Brass Perfects

A001	2000 - 2500
A002	2500 - 3000
A003	2000 - 2500
A004	2500 - 3000
A005	3000 - 3500
A006	3500 - 4500
A007	2500 - 3000
A008	5000 - 6000
A009	5000 - 6000
A010	1000 - 1500
A011	1500 - 1800
A012	1500 - 2000
A013	1800 - 2400
A014	2200 - 2500
A015	2000 - 2500
A016	5000 - 6000
A017	2000 - 2500
A018	6000 - 8000
A019	2000 - 2500
A020	3000 - 3500
A021	4500 - 5500

Section B
Brass Faced Perfects

B100	400 - 500
B101	300 - 400
B102	500 - 600
B103	600 - 700
B104	1500 - 2000
B105	800 - 1200
B106	1200 - 1500
B107	2500 - 3000
B108	500 - 600
B109	1500 - 2000
B110	1800 - 2200
B111	1000 - 1500
B112	700 - 1000
B113	700 - 1000
B114	1000 - 1500
B115	1200 - 1500
B116	600 - 700
B117	700 – 800

Section C
Alloy Perfects

C150	2500 - 3000
C151	600 - 800
C152	400 - 450
C153	3000 - 3500
C154	1200 - 1600
C155	500 - 600
C156	800 - 1000
C157	300 - 400
C158	400 - 600
C159	700 - 1000
C160	400 - 500
C161	500 - 600
C162	200 - 300
C163	500 - 600
C164	400 - 600
C165	250 - 300
C166	600 - 700
C167	1300 - 1800
C168	700 - 1000
C169	700 - 800
C170	500 - 600
C171	2000 - 2500
C172	350 - 400
C173	450 - 600
C174	400 - 500
C175	500 - 600
C176	300 - 400
C177	2000 - 2500
C178	250 - 350
C179	500 - 600
C180	450 - 550
C181	500 - 600

Section D
Bouglé

D200	1500 - 1800
D201	2000 - 2500
D202	1800 - 2200

Section E
Brass

E250	400 - 600
E251	200 - 300
E252	400 - 500
E253	2000 - 2500
E254	150 - 200
E255	150 - 200
E256	300 - 350
E257	350 - 450
E258	300 - 350
E259	300 - 400
E260	450 - 600
E261	300 - 400
E262	300 – 400

Section F
St.George

F300	300 - 400
F301	3000 - 3500
F302	200 - 250
F303	300 - 400
F304	120 - 170
F305	400 - 500
F306	200 - 280
F307	750 - 1000
F308	750 - 1000
F309	450 - 550
F310	600 - 700
F311	1500 - 2000
F312	2500 - 3000

Section G
Uniqua

G350	200 - 250
G351	100 - 130
G352	120 - 140
G353	80 - 100
G354	180 - 220
G355	180 - 200

Section H
Field

H375	400 - 500
H376	1200 - 1800

Section I
Barton

I400	2000 - 3000

Section J			Q601	200 - 250		Section V	

Section J
Tournament
J425   2000 - 2500

Section K
St.John
K450   150 - 200
K451   150 - 200
K452   500 - 600

Section L
Davy
L475   1500 - 2500

Section M
Sunbeam
M500   80 - 120
M501   70 - 100

Section N
Hydra
N525   30 - 70
N526   50 - 100

Section O
Lightweight
O550   450 - 500

Section P
Silex
P575   170 - 250
P576   300 - 350
P577   200 - 250
P578   170 - 200
P579   400 - 600

Section Q
Silex No.2
Q600   120 - 170

Q601   200 - 250
Q602   300 - 400
Q603   700 - 850
Q604   750 - 900
Q605   250 - 350
Q606   500 - 700

Section R
Silex Major
R650   300 - 400
R651   200 - 300
R652   300 - 350
R653   170 - 200
R654   200 - 250
R655   200 - 270
R656   200 - 1000

Section S
Silex Multiplier
S700   800 - 1200
S701   1000 - 1500
S702   800 - 1200

Section T
Super Silex
T750   250 - 350
T751   400 - 600
T752   700 - 900
T753   600 - 800
T754   350 - 450

Section U
Centrepin
U800   600 - 800
U801   800 - 1200
U802   250 - 300
U803   150 - 200
U804   150 - 200

Section V
Presentation
V850   4000 - 5000

Section W
Sea
W900   500 - 600
W901   1000 - 1500
W902   500 - 700
W903   200 - 300
W904   2000 - 3000
W905   4000 - 6000
W906   2500 - 3500
W907   4000 - 5000

Section X
Altex & Hardex
X950   70 - 100
X951   350 - 450
X952   80 - 120
X953   130 - 160
X954   60 - 80
X955   80 - 120
X956   500 - 700

Section Y
Multiplying Baitcasters
Y1000   80 - 130
Y1001   1500 - 2000
Y1002   800 - 1200
Y1003   600 - 700

Section Z
Cascapedia
Z1050   6000 - 7000

Tips on Collecting:

When building a collection always secure items that are in or closest to original condition and be prepared to pay slightly over the odds for them because these will rise in value faster than items that are not in good condition. The exceptions to this rule are things that are extremely rare, which should first be secured and upgraded later, if at all possible.

Upgrading your collection is important. If you see an item in much better condition than one you already own you should buy it and sell the old one. This process of upgrading will eventually result in your collection becoming top grade and consequently enjoying top value.

Never polish reels, especially those made of brass. As you can see from the examples in this book brass reels had a dark bronzed finish applied to them, many with a lacquer over the top. Ideally this is the condition you want the reels in your collection to be in. Once a brass reel has had the bronzing polished away it has been greatly devalued. Duralumin reels with no applied finish did come polished, but if re-polishing is required this needs to be carried out by a specialist metal polisher or the reel may be devalued.

Unless there is something drastically wrong with reels and urgent attention is needed a good rule is to leave them well alone, simply clean them with a very lightly oiled soft cloth and keep them in a dry environment.

Beware of leaving finger marks on reels. These carry salt and will eat into the finish. Wear soft cotton gloves or at the very least make sure you wipe your reels down with a lightly oiled cloth after handling.

Hardy Lure Price Guide 2004

Note: Prices should be taken as a guide only as lures sell above and below these guide prices and lure values depend upon a number of factors including size, rarity and condition and lures that are boxed or on original cards and in mint, unused condition are the most valuable.

Guide prices are in Pounds Sterling, please use the prevailing exchange rate to calculate the value in your country. Lures are listed in the same order as in the book.

30 - 50	Phantom Minnow	300 - 400	Alnwick Spinner if marked Hardy's
30 - 50	SoleSkin Phantom	120 - 150	Hog Backed Pattern Spoon large
30 - 50	M.C.Patent Phantom		if stamped Hardy's
40 - 60	Horn Phantom	80 - 120	Hog Backed Pattern Spoon small
40 - 60	Rubber Phantom		if stamped Hardy's
25 - 50	Special Phantom	15 - 30	Special Extra Heavy Spoon
20 - 40	Ideal Phantom	50 - 70	Kidney/Special Spoon Tiger Fish
120 - 150	Chilwa Phantom	80 - 120	Hog Back Flying Bar Spoon
120 - 150	Hardy Phantom 1910 Model	80 - 120	Hog-Back Revolving Spoon
30 - 50	Hardy Anti-Kink Phantom	25 - 40	Hog-Backed Mahseer
25 - 50	Hutton Wye Phantom		Spoons early
40 - 65	Anti-Kink Devon 1914 Model	12 - 20	Hog-Backed Spoons late
50 - 75	Flat Head Keel Head (early)	100 - 150	Hardy Professional Spoon
80 - 120	Forward Devon	12 - 20	Norwegian Scaled Spoon
200 - 250	Amber Devon small	15 - 25	Bergen Spoon
250 - 350	Amber Devon large	15 - 25	Special Extra Heavy Kidney
350 - 450	Amber Devon Maori Inanga		Spoons
25 - 30	Pennell, fluted end	25 - 40	Wilson Spoon
30 - 50	Aluminium Pennell	35 - 45	Stewart Spoon Large
20 - 30	Improved Pennell	25 - 35	Stewart Spoon Small
50 - 80	Pennell, Mahseer	30 - 50	Silver Devon Bar Spoon early
12 - 20	Pennell Threadline	25 - 40	Silver Devon Bar Spoon middle
25 - 40	Pioneer Devon	10 - 20	Silver Devon Bar Spoon late
12 - 20	Aluminium Pioneer	40 - 60	Indian Spoon large
20 - 30	Improved Pioneer Devon	8 - 12	Tube Spoon
15 - 25	Quill Devon	30 - 50	Jim Vincent Broads Spoon
50 - 80	Beadnell Spinner	8 - 12	Greenwell Spoon
15 - 25	Golden Sprat Devon early	100 - 150	Pearl Devon White large
10 - 15	Golden Sprat Devon 1950's	80 - 120	Pearl Devon White small
200 - 250	Herring/Sprat Bait large	200 - 250	Pink Pearl Devon Pink large
20 - 40	Herring/Sprat Bait small	100 - 150	Pink Pearl Devon Pink small
25 - 40	Wetheral	80 - 100	Pearl Spoon large
20 - 30	Murdoch Oval Devon	60 - 80	Pearl Spoon small
10 - 15	Heavyweight Devon	80 - 100	Pearl Spoon Experimental
15 - 25	Reflex Devon	80 - 120	Darting and Diving Bait Large
8 - 12	Sprat-Devon	40 - 80	Darting and Diving Bait Small
8 - 12	West Country Devon	50 - 80	Hardy Wiggler
15 - 25	Rose's Reversible	15 - 30	Hardy Jock Scott Wiggler Large
15 - 25	Strathallan Devon	10 - 15	Hardy Jock Scott Wiggler Small
20 - 30	Wood Devon	30 - 50	Wake Lure
15 - 25	Flat Bodied Devon	30 - 50	No.2 Wake Lure
25 - 40	1909 Model Fly Minnow large	40 - 60	Flexible Sprat Bait
15 - 25	1909 Model Fly Minnow small	20 - 30	Flexible Sprat Blue and Silver
15 - 25	Fly Minnow	15 - 30	Halcyon original
50 - 70	Swallow Tail large	20 - 40	Halcyon improved
25 - 35	Swallow Tail small	800 - 1200	Halcyon improved large
25 - 40	Swimmer Bait	25 - 40	Sylph Minnow
25 - 35	Hardy Spoon early	40 - 60	Soleskin Sprat or Brit
15 - 25	Hardy Spoon late	25 - 40	Silver Sand Eel (soleskin)